Jim Clyman

Also by the author:

JEDEDIAH SMITH: Trail Blazer of the West

Jim Clyman

by Hal G. Evarts

G. P. Putnam's Sons   New York

Library of Congress Catalog Card
Number: 59-11430

Manufactured in the United States of America
Van Rees Press · New York

CONTENTS

Jim Clyman

1. THE FIRST STEP WEST

Hugging his rifle under one arm, Jim Clyman hurried toward the wagon. Today was the day! This sunny June morning of 1807 the Clyman family was moving west, leaving their Virginia farm behind and moving west across the mountains into the Ohio wilderness, as so many of their neighbors had done before. Jim could hardly wait.

He was six feet tall and thin as a sprouting weed, with blue eyes and sandy hair. At sixteen he was already a crack shot and expert hunter. The family depended on Jim's sure eye for much of their meat. Until today he'd never been beyond the peaceful valley where he was born. But now all the strange unknown land across the Blue Ridge Mountains was calling to him.

9

His mother and little sisters climbed into the wagon. His brothers John and Lancaster were stowing away the last of their treasures. His father shut the door on the empty house and put a hand on Jim's shoulder. In a quiet serious voice he said, "You're the oldest, Jim. You're strong for your age. You've had some schooling and you've got a level head."

"Yes, sir."

"We're turning our backs on our home," his father went on, "and starting a long journey. There'll be many a hardship and danger ahead. But I want you young'uns to have a chance in the new country that's opening up."

The Clymans were poor. One wagon held everything they owned. Even the farm was a leasehold, that had once belonged to George Washington himself. Many a time as a small awe-struck boy, in this very yard, Jim had heard the great man tell of his experiences fighting Indians "out yonder" beyond the mountains. Tales of that wild frontier had grown in his imagination till he was fit to bust.

"From now on you'll have a man's job, a man's responsibilities. I'm counting on you, Jim."

All his life Jim was to remember these words of

10

his father's. He liked farming. He loved to read, especially poetry. He might become a surveyor, like George Washington, or a soldier. The thought of fighting painted Indians made him shiver. But best of all, he guessed, he'd like to keep on going west, into the sun, as far as he could travel.

"Hi-yup!" his father shouted at the oxen. The heavy wagon creaked and began to roll. His mother was crying softly as she waved at the friends who had gathered to say good-by. Proudly Jim strode along beside the team. No sad farewells for him. Five hundred miles to Ohio and he'd walk every step.

At the turning on the hill he looked back for a glimpse of the farm he would never see again. He had no way of foretelling the future. But within a few years he would be a farmer, surveyor and soldier too. He would become one of the greatest Indian fighters of his time. Jim Clyman was heading west.

Hundreds of other families were on the move that summer, all seeking cheap land that was said to be rich beyond belief. Some, like Jim, were seeking adventure and excitement. They traveled together in slow-moving wagon trains that stirred up clouds of dust and covered only a few miles each day over the rough mountain roads. They crawled across the Appalachians and crept down toward the little town of Pittsburgh, where an early frost turned the forests into blazing color.

Here Jim's father decided to winter. So it was not until the following spring that the Clymans reached their destination and settled near Sandy Creek in northeastern Ohio. They rented some land that was already cleared, built a cabin and planted their crop. That first year Jim was so busy he had no time to be restless. With the other boys he worked from dark till dark, then staggered to his corn-husk ticking in the loft and fell asleep. His life wasn't adventuresome at all, not a bit like he'd dreamed.

But the second year, after the harvest was in, he wandered alone through the deep silent woods that were so different from his native Virginia. He collected nuts, hunted squirrels and deer, learned how to tree a possum and imitate a turkey call. He taught himself to read sign and to trap muskrat and raccoon along the creeks. At eighteen he was mastering the woodcraft skills that were to save his life many times in the days ahead.

The nearest neighbor was several miles away, the nearest settlement half a day on horseback. But there were other visitors who came slipping out of the forest to the Clyman cabin. Indians. At first most were friendly, members of the Miami, Delaware and

Shawnee tribes, who wanted to trade their furs and hides for blankets and tools and sugar. Some begged for food. Then one day a passing buck tried to steal an ax, and Mr. Clyman drove him off at rifle point.

Ever since the first white man entered the Ohio Valley there had been trouble with Indians, off and on. Now the tribes grew bitter toward the settlers who were plowing up their hunting grounds. They began to raid and burn and kill, striking terror throughout the territory. Rumors spread. Some people believed that the British in Canada were stirring up the Indians, arming them to drive out the Americans. Any day now, they said, the English and their red allies would declare war.

One November afternoon Jim was returning with a load of supplies when John ran out to meet him. "Father's just bought a quarter section over in Stark County," John said. "Our own land. We're moving."

But Jim had more important news. "General Harrison had a big scrap with redskins out west at Tippecanoe," he told his brother. "Licked 'em too."

John's eyes grew round. "Then it *is* war!"

"Looks that way," Jim said. "By jings, I'd sure like to go."

But he was needed more than ever during the next few months. While other young men answered

13

the call for volunteers and drilled with the militia, Jim had to help clear the new land. He felled trees and burned stumps and hauled rocks. During those dark trying days he worked as he'd never worked before. News was weeks late in reaching their lonely cabin but word finally came that war had broken out between England and the United States, the War of 1812.

The militia shouldered their muskets and marched off to fight. General Hull, so the talk went, was leading his Ohio Volunteers north to smash the British in Canada. They'd whip the redcoats first, then punish the savages once and for all. Grimly Jim kept at his chores with his rifle always loaded.

One night late in August a rider raced into the clearing. "Best pack up your family and clear out!" he panted. "The English captured Hull and took Detroit. Injuns'll be swarming over the whole countryside."

He hurried on to spread the alarm, and next day most of the Clymans' neighbors loaded up their wagons and moved away to the safety of the large settlements. Only a few chose to stay behind and defend their homes, Jim's father among them. "We've worked five long years for this land," he declared. "We'll fight for it if we have to."

Jim was proud of him. But he couldn't sit back any longer, not with most of the able-bodied men off at war. He had to do his part, however small. "They're organizing Committees of Safety, Father," he said. "They need riders. You can spare me, now the boys are big enough to help protect the farm."

Reluctantly his father agreed. He'd fought against the British in the Revolution. "I hoped my sons would never have to fight a war," he said. "But God go with you, Jim."

So Jim rode off to become a Ranger. He had to provide his own horse and weapons, and he served without pay or uniform. Emboldened by the British victory, the Indians began to raid again, massacring and scalping isolated settlers all across Ohio, Indiana and Michigan. Jim's job was to carry messages from town to town and alert his fellow Rangers, so they could pursue the raiders.

For weeks he was in the saddle almost constantly, pounding along the roads and trails, catching a few winks of sleep whenever he could. The Indians seemed to be everywhere. They attacked in small bands, then melted away in the forest. It was an endless, heartbreaking task, like chasing shadows.

One frosty moonlit night, when Jim was riding toward a ford, a bunch of Indians leaped out of the

15

brush ahead, screeching and shaking their tomahawks. His heart gave a jump. The enemy at last,
face to face! The trail was too narrow to turn. He
had no time to think. Kicking his horse in the ribs,
he galloped straight at the astounded Indians and
fired his rifle.

They scattered to one side and Jim drew his pistol.
The horse was flying now and as Jim ran between
them he swung his rifle at the nearest Indian. The
red man dodged and let out a howl of rage, but
Jim was safely past. He splashed across the creek
and raced on through the woods, confident they
wouldn't follow him on foot. The would-be ambush
was over so quickly he could scarcely believe it had
happened.

When he reached the settlement at daybreak his
captain was waiting anxiously. "It's a wonder you
got through last night, Jim boy," he exclaimed. "Redskins thick as fleas."

The captain listened to Jim's story and nodded ap-
proval. "That was a close scrape! You must've been
scared."

"Scared green," Jim admitted with a grin. "But
one thing I know now."

"What's that, Jim?"

"Never let an Indian know you're scared." He'd

been thinking about his escape ever since. To stay alive on this frontier you had to keep learning, find a lesson in each new experience. And that was the hardest school of all—Indian warfare. "If you do, you're a goner sure."

Two days later, returning with more dispatches, he observed a column of black smoke. Cautiously approaching through the trees, Jim crept up on a small clearing. He was too late. Raiders had come and gone, firing the cabin and butchering the livestock. The farmer, his wife and four young children lay in pools of blood. In horror Jim stared at the mutilated bodies, and tears filled his eyes.

This might have been his own family, innocent settlers who had harmed no one. Among the smoldering ruins he found a shovel with a charred handle and scooped out a grave. Bareheaded in the autumn sunlight, he said a prayer for these poor victims. And when he rode on about his military duties, Jim Clyman was no longer a greenhorn youngster who looked upon war as a big adventure. He was a man who had seen its ugly brutal side. And he vowed to keep on fighting until the last hostile Indian was driven from Ohio, until this land was safe for all Americans.

Shortly afterward troops arrived from Pennsylvania and took over the job of defending the frontier. The Indians fled. Jim's Ranger company was disbanded. Nobody made speeches or gave any medals, but this handful of men had served their country well in a time of desperate need. Their courage and hard-riding devotion had saved the lives of hundreds of settlers.

Jim at once enlisted in the militia. Much to his disgust he was assigned garrison duty far from any fighting. He trained and drilled and guarded depots of arms. And he learned another lesson—that much of a soldier's life is spent waiting for battles that may never occur. The lesson of preparedness.

The war dragged to a close. After two years a treaty was signed between England and America. Peace had come again. Jim was free to return to the farm, to take up his old life.

2. FREEDOM

Dᴜʀɪɴɢ his absence his father had died, and on Jim's shoulders fell the load of looking after the family—his mother, younger brothers and sisters. Times were hard as a result of the war and cash money was so scarce that the Clymans had to barter their crops and produce for the goods they needed. Soon Stark County began to fill up with land-hungry settlers from the Atlantic seaboard.

Where Jim once had wandered through virgin forests, hunting and trapping and fishing, there now were farms everywhere. The wilderness was gone. With each new homestead crowding in he grew more restless, eager to push beyond the fringe of civilization. He could understand how the Indians before him must have felt. But for four years he put aside

19

his hopes while he worked the farm and saw to it that the younger Clymans got a proper start in life.

Other men his age married, settled down and raised families of their own. Not Jim Clyman. He was twenty-seven years old and had never been west of Ohio. But when the time came—

In the spring of 1818 his brother John finally said, "Why don't you cut loose, Jim? Lan and I, we're not kids. We can get along without you now."

Jim hesitated. The farm was prosperous. His sisters were almost grown. The thickets where bloodthirsty savages once lay in wait had given way to villages and plowed fields. For the first time since that long-ago day when he'd left Virginia he felt truly free.

"Go on," John urged him. "You've an itchy foot, Jim. You're not cut out to be a farmer like the rest of us."

So Jim set out with a horse and rifle and a few belongings. He wanted to see the country, keep his eyes open for any opportunity that might arise. Day after day he rode on toward the southwest, camping in the open each night, until he had left the thickly settled regions far behind. Even the air seemed fresher out where a man could travel for miles and never see a road or fence rail.

Finally in a hilly section of southern Indiana he

Freedom

found some land to his liking and cleared a small tract. There was plenty of game and fur along the creek bottoms. His only neighbors were a friendly tribe of Delaware Indians, who had been forced to move west after the war. Jim wintered there, enjoying his solitude, and the next spring planted a crop of corn.

Only an occasional traveler rode by, but shortly before harvest time a wagon rolled up to his field and stopped. A woman and several children peered out from under the canvas and a man stepped down. "Looks like good rich land," he said.

"You're not planning to settle hereabouts, are you?" Jim asked.

"Reckon so, mister. 'Less you've got some objections."

Jim wasn't very happy, but he grinned. Behind this wagon there'd be another. And another. The whole Ohio Valley was filling up. Before long these hills would be solid with cabins. "Tell you what," he said. "I spent a year chopping trees and grubbing with a hoe. You help me pick this harvest and you can have my clearing."

"What's wrong with it?"

"Nothing," Jim told him. "But it's getting crowded."

21

So Jim got rid of his farm. The following week he got rid of his corn. He traded the whole crop to the Delawares for eight Indian ponies. Footloose once more, he felt he'd made a good exchange.

Riding back to the nearest settlement, he sold his ponies and hired out to a land surveyor named Morris. In his spare time he carried the rod and chain, and learned how to use a transit. When Morris fell sick, Jim knew enough to finish up subdividing a township. This bit of knowledge proved to be a turning point in his career.

Restless as ever, he pushed on west into the prairies of Illinois, and soon found himself broke again. This time he took the unlikely job of keeping books for a salt works. He had been there several months when a stranger came to his room. "I'm Colonel William Hamilton," the man said, "government land surveyor."

Jim shook hands. The colonel, he knew, was the son of the great Alexander Hamilton, drafter of the federal Constitution and first Treasurer of the United States. "The Government in Washington," Colonel Hamilton explained, "is anxious to survey all this land above the Ohio as soon as possible. Thousands of settlers are pouring in here. It's a big important job, and I need men I can depend on."

Jim was flattered, but he said, "I'm not a real surveyor, Colonel. I've only done a smattering."

"I'll teach you all you need to know. The important thing you already know: how to get along in the wilderness. You see, Mr. Clyman, I've heard a great deal about you."

Delighted, Jim quit his clerical job and hastened north with Hamilton and his party to the Vermilion River. Within a few weeks he acquired enough skill at his new trade so that the colonel put him in full charge. He liked the constant change and moving about. It gave him a sense of achievement to open up new lands for the growing tide of emigrants, although he had no desire to settle himself.

Next year Hamilton sent him farther west, to survey a tract along the Sangamon River. By now Jim was an expert. He might have made this his life's work, except for a chance that took him to St. Louis. To collect the back pay due him he had to report to the nearest government office.

That winter of 1823, when he stepped ashore from a Mississippi River raft, St. Louis was a booming town of five thousand people. It was a hub of inland commerce and the jumping-off place for the fur trade. Fortunes were made and lost overnight. Here gaunt leathery men in buckskins, the Rocky Mountain

23

trappers, outfitted and set out up the Missouri for the Far West. Jim was spellbound by all the bustle.

Not long after he arrived a Negro slave delivered a note inviting him to call on William H. Ashley. Ashley, he learned, was a general in the state militia and lieutenant governor of Missouri. Puzzled, Jim wondered what such a prominent man could want with him.

General Ashley, a fellow Virginian, greeted Jim warmly. "My friend Colonel Hamilton recommended you, Mr. Clyman," he said. "I think you're just the man I'm looking for."

"You need a surveyor, General?"

Ashley handed him a newspaper clipping. "Read this first."

It was an advertisement from the St. Louis *Enquirer*. Jim read:

TO

ENTERPRISING YOUNG MEN

The subscriber wishes to engage ONE HUNDRED MEN to ascend the river Missouri to its source, there to be employed for one, two or three years. Wages to be paid in the amount of two hundred dollars per annum. For particulars inquire of the subscriber.

(Signed) WM. H. ASHLEY.

Jim listened while the general explained. The rivers and creeks of the western mountains abounded in beaver. The skins of these beautiful animals, in demand throughout the world for men's fur hats, sold for six dollars a piece. A man could make himself rich in one season. The profits were great, but so were the dangers. Most of the country beyond the Mississippi was unexplored, full of savage Indians and the ferocious grizzly bear. The life of a trapper was hard and lonely, with the risk of violent death ever present.

The year before, Ashley and his partner had built a fort far to the northwest, at the mouth of the Yellowstone River. Now he was forming a second expedition, gathering supplies and trade goods to ship to his trappers already there. But what he needed most, the general said, was men. Good trustworthy men who wouldn't desert at the first sign of trouble. Mountain men who could shoot straight and stand up to the perils of a vast unknown wilderness.

"I'll be frank, Mr. Clyman. Such men are scarce. That's why I sent for you."

With a stir of excitement Jim stared at the map on Ashley's wall. Much of it was blank, with only a line here and there to indicate a river or mountain range. There wasn't a town for thousands of miles, clear to the Pacific Ocean. Suddenly he longed to travel that land beyond the Shining Mountains. All his wanderings and frontier experience had fitted him for this moment. Thrusting out his hand, he said, "I'm your man, sir."

"Splendid!" Ashley clapped him on the shoulder. In the first minute he had sized up this quiet, calm-eyed Virginian as a leader who would make his mark anywhere. A shrewd judge of men, he knew how lucky he was to sign on Jim Clyman. "Welcome to the Rocky Mountain Fur Company."

Details were quickly settled. Jim would be paid one dollar a day. In addition he would receive his food, traps, powder and shot for his rifle, and was to keep for himself half the beaver he caught. His first job, here in St. Louis, was to recruit some more "enterprising young men." The general led him to a nearby house, headquarters for the expedition, and introduced a burly dark-bearded man. "This is Moses Harris," Ashley said, "but everybody calls him 'Black.' He's the walkingest man in Missouri."

Black Harris chuckled. "Howdy, Jim. Fetch in your possibles and make yourself to home."

In turn he introduced Jim to the others: grizzled Hugh Glass; solemn young David Jackson; John Gardner and Henry Fraeb. All had been up the Missouri before. They would be his companions in the months to come. "You ever cotched beaver before, Jim?" Hugh Glass asked.

Jim shook his head. A newcomer to the fur trade, he still had to prove himself to these veterans. But, like General Ashley, they saw he was no tenderfoot. "I'll show you how, ole hoss," Black said. "Reckon you'll do to ride the river with."

True to his word, Black helped him equip. The most important purchase was a heavy flintlock Hawken rifle, designed to hunt the big game of the West, such as buffalo, elk and grizzly. Jim bought a "Green River" skinning knife, a new powder horn and bullet mold. His boots and woolen clothes he discarded for moccasins and fringed buckskins, practical for a trapper who would spend hours each day in water. These items, together with personal gear—sewing kit, his diary, and a volume of Shakespeare's poetry crammed into one small bag—would make up his total outfit for the next few years.

Then he turned to the task of finding recruits. Three other rival companies were scouring the town, in a race to set off for the fur country first, and competition was fierce. Down on the tough brawling riverfront, Jim went through the taverns and grog-shops. He hired boatmen from New Orleans, Tennessee backwoodsmen, Illinois farmers, loggers from New England—a cross-section of lusty young America.

Among others he persuaded to join the expedition were Bill Sublette, a lanky hunter from Kentucky, and a red-cheeked Irishman named Tom Fitzpatrick. These two, along with Reed Gibson of Virginia, soon became Jim's close friends. Like himself they were educated, itching for adventure. For interpreter he secured the services of a famous mountain man, Edward Rose, who was part Negro and part Indian, known as Cutnose because the tip of his nose had been bitten off in a fight.

When he had rounded up about seventy men Jim reported back to Ashley. "I've scraped the bottom of the barrel, General," he said. "A lot of 'em are cut-throats and gumboes, but they'll make you a fighting crew."

"You can handle them, Jim," Ashley said. "I'm putting you second in command."

Meanwhile Davy Jackson, in charge of supplies, had been loading up two keelboats for the long river journey. Pork and corn meal, kegs of gun-powder, lead bars, barrels of whisky and trade goods for the Indians. All the many things a fur brigade would need for survival were carefully stored aboard the *Yellowstone Packet* and *The Rocky Mountains*. Finally, after weeks of preparation, the general called his men together and announced they would leave next day.

John Gardner tossed his hat in the air with a whoop. "Wagh, we're off for the mountings, boys! Hooraw for beaver tail!"

"Faith be, Jim," Tom Fitzpatrick said in his Irish brogue. "Why such a long face?"

Jim smiled. All winter long, rumors of Indian trouble had been filtering down from the mountains. Rough and willing many of these men might be, but few actually had fought against Indians. "It's a big moment, Tom. Seems like I've been waiting all my life for this. But I wonder how many of our friends will ever see St. Louis again."

On the raw blustery morning of March 10 they boarded their boats. Crowds lined the riverfront. Parents and wives and sweethearts called tearful good-bys to their loved ones, who might be gone for years. General Ashley gave the signal. The boatmen, red-hatted French-Canadian *voyageurs,* poled off into the Mississippi and hoisted sail. A swivel gun boomed in salute and Old Glory rippled in the wind.

Standing alone in the bow, Jim drew a deep breath

29

as the wooded hills slid by. He'd come a long way from Virginia, but the journey was only beginning. Ahead lay the Big Muddy, leading into the heart of the unknown.

3. THE REE MASSACRE

Jim soon learned how to move heavily laden keelboats against the Missouri's mighty current. Whenever the wind failed, the crew poled the clumsy craft upriver. Most of the time, however, they had to cordelle. They tied a long rope to the mast, scrambled ashore and towed the two boats along the bank by sheer muscle power. It was a slow backbreaking task and some days they gained only a mile or two.

More than once they ran aground on sandbars and had to lighten cargo to work free. There were other hazards to navigation: violent storms, bluffs that caved in without warning, floating logs, and the dreaded sawyers—submerged trees that could rip a boat to pieces. But steadily they made their way

31

west across the state of Missouri and passed the last American settlement. With every bend of the river civilization fell farther astern.

It was a strange new world to Jim and each night, when they tied up to camp, he sat by the fire and wrote his impressions in his journal. Some of the men complained at the hard work, and a few sneaked off into the brush and deserted. By the time they reached Fort Atkinson, a new post the Army had built to hold the Indians in check, the expedition had lost ten employees. To fill their place Jim hired several ex-soldiers who wanted to become trappers.

And here they received a warning. Colonel Leavenworth, the commanding officer, told them, "You may have trouble up ahead. Warfare has broken out between the Sioux and the Rees."

"I traded with both those tribes last year," Ashley said, "and plan to again. They seemed friendly."

"All the same, be on your guard," the colonel advised.

They pushed on through a country of vast treeless prairies and Jim had the thrill of seeing his first buffalo, a great shaggy herd that made the earth tremble when they stampeded. And later, at Fort Kiowa, a trading post of the Missouri Fur Company, he saw his first Sioux. The most feared warriors of the plains, they were superb horsemen who lived to hunt buffalo and raid their enemies. So far they had been friendly to Americans.

Jim and General Ashley made presents to their chief and smoked the peace pipe. But the post factor warned them again. Only two months earlier the Aricaras, or Rees, mortal enemies of the Sioux, had attacked the fort and been driven off. During the fight a son of the Ree chief, Gray Eyes, had been killed. Now Gray Eyes was seeking revenge.

"Surely Gray Eyes has no cause to fight me," Ashley said. "My men had no part in his son's death."

"They say he's turned against all white men," the factor declared. "Rees have a record of treachery."

Several nights later the expedition received a third warning. They were camped along the bank when a canoe glided out of the darkness and a tall young man stepped up to the fire. After a hearty welcome, Ashley introduced him. "This is Jedediah Smith, my stout right arm. Meet Jim Clyman. You two get acquainted, 'cause you'll be working together."

They shook hands. Jim had heard much about Prayin' Jed Smith, and liked him at once.

"Jed's a lot like you, Jim," the general went on. "Always has his nose in a book. Never talks much. But when trouble's afoot—look out!"

Quickly Jed told his story. He was carrying a message from Andrew Henry, the general's partner, far upriver at the Yellowstone. The trappers needed many horses. Hiding by day and paddling by night, Jed had slipped through Ree territory undetected. But in the past few weeks the Rees had heavily fortified their two big villages on the river bank.

"They talk peace, sir," Jed concluded, "but they're getting ready for war."

"We'll have to take that chance," Ashley decided. "They have the horses we need. It's too late to turn back."

Late in May the *Yellowstone Packet* and *The Rocky Mountains* cautiously approached the Ree settlement and anchored in midstream. With curiosity Jim studied the high stockade, built of logs and interwoven willow branches, which protected the villages. They commanded the narrow river channel and the strip of beach below. His experience as a soldier told him that here was a formidable fort.

Not one Indian stepped out to greet the expedition. In ominous silence General Ashley and Jim, with Jed Smith and Cutnose, rowed ashore, covered by the rifles of their waiting men. Presently two chiefs, Gray Eyes and Little Soldier, came to parley. Through the gate Jim got a glimpse of their huts, heaps of dirt and brush that looked like huge potato mounds. Unlike the wandering Sioux, the Rees were farmers, who grew corn in the fields surrounding their stout picket walls.

Surly and suspicious, the two chiefs demanded what the white men wanted. "Tell them," Ashley ordered his interpreter, "that we come in peace. We will pay well for horses."

After a conference in grunts and sign language, Cutnose said, "Gray Eyes has agreed. They'll open trading with us tomorrow morning."

"You see!" Ashley exclaimed. "They mean us no harm."

But Jim was not so sure. And his misgivings grew after they returned to the keelboats. During that afternoon dozens of Ree braves paddled across the river and hid themselves on a bluff. Now it would be impossible to pole or cordelle without being caught in a crossfire from both banks. As Jim told Jed Smith, "I tried to persuade the general to move downriver to a safer place. Maybe you can reason with him."

Jed shook his head. "He's a stubborn man, Jim. I don't trust those Rees either. We'll have to be on our toes."

At daybreak, after a sleepless night, Jim had

several skiffloads of goods ferried over to the beach, where a throng of Indians waited. There were hundreds, accompanied by squaws and naked children and packs of scrawny dogs. Almost half the bucks, he noticed, carried English muzzle loaders. Trading went on slowly—blankets and axes, mirrors and beads and froofraw for the women. By sundown, when Gray Eyes and his people withdrew behind their stockade, the general had only nineteen horses, not half enough.

"We'll swim this bunch across the river now," Ashley said, "and buy the rest tomorrow."

But a sudden storm sprang up, rain and lightning and wind that lashed the water into waves. Soaked to the skin, Jim told the general, "We can't move the horses tonight. I'd better bring in more men to guard them, this close to the Rees."

Ashley nodded. "I'll leave you and Jed in charge."

Out aboard the *Packet* Jim named the cream of the crew—his friend Reed Gibson, Bill Sublette, Tom Fitzpatrick, John Gardner—about forty men. Back on the wet dark beach again, he and Jed organized them for defense. They moved the horses back from the fort, dug shallow trenches and piled up driftwood. Jim sent Cutnose and Aaron Stephens to scout around the lower village.

"I don't like this a bit, Jed," he said. "The general traded those Rees too much powder and lead today. They're well armed, and they outnumber us twenty to one."

At first light, Jed agreed, they must swim the horses downstream beyond rifle or bowshot. Meanwhile, all they could do was huddle in the sand, trapped between the river and the Indian stockade. Jim crawled from man to man, making sure that each had dry powder and flints. Then an uproar broke out near the village and Cutnose sprinted down the slope.

"They caught Stephens!" he panted. "Stabbed him dead and lifted his hair!"

"Them red varmints!" growled Hugh Glass. "Let's go burn out their pesthole!"

"Hold on, Hugh," Jim said. "We can't help poor Aaron now. Our job is to hold this beach and protect the horses."

After some argument the others sided with Jim. To attack the stockade would be foolish. Up behind the walls drums were thumping and wild yells and chants filled the night. From their loopholes the Indians shouted down taunts and worked themselves to a frenzy. "No redskin kin rub out this coon," John Gardner muttered.

"We'll fight if we have to," Jim said grimly. "If they think we're afraid, they'll butcher us all."

At last the sky began to pale. Suddenly a rifle crackled from the village. Then another. A terrified horse bolted across the sand and collapsed. In an instant the air was full of bullets and whizzing arrows. Jim saw it was too late to save the herd. "Take cover!" he shouted. "Keep down!"

He jumped behind one of the fallen ponies, took careful aim and squeezed his trigger. A warrior toppled down from the stockade. Jim's men were firing as fast as they could reload, but the Rees, sheltered behind their log wall, made poor targets. Trapper after trapper fell as a murderous fire raked the beach. Cries of the wounded and dying rose above the roar of guns.

"Send in the skiffs," Jim yelled. "Take off the wounded."

But out aboard the keelboats all was confusion. Men ran up and down the deck while General Ashley bellowed orders at them. Finally one skiff, manned by four *voyageurs,* skimmed in to shore. Jim grabbed a wounded trapper under the arms and dragged him toward the boat. John Gardner ran to give him a hand and fell with an arrow in his chest.

Other skiffs tried to relieve the beach, but a storm

38

of lead drove them back. Now the defenders, reduced by nearly half, were cut off from help. A fierce pride gripped Jim. These were *his* men, his recruits from the sinks and saloons of St. Louis. Greenhorns many might be, but not a one had panicked. They fought bravely, like campaign veterans, against tremendous odds.

"Look to yore topknot, lad!" Hugh Glass roared. "Hyar they come!"

Indians were streaming out of the stockade with howls of fury. Hastily Jim and the others piled up a breastwork of dead horses. But the Rees split and crept through the cornfields on both flanks, pouring in their deadly fire. Three more trappers went down. And now Jim realized the bitter truth. To stay any longer was to sacrifice his men. They must abandon the beach or be massacred.

"Take to the water! Every man for himself."

Some men dropped before they reached the river. Others paddled a few strokes and sank. Jim rammed one more bullet down his barrel and took a final shot at the charging horde of Rees. He and Jed, the last to leave, raced to the bank. Jim shoved his rifle muzzle down under his belt and leaped. Cold muddy water closed over his head.

Jim surfaced and struck out for the nearest skiff,

but the current spun him away into midstream. From shore the Indians peppered the water around him with bullets. Jim dove deep, holding his breath until he had to come up for air. But the weight of the heavy Hawken sucked him under again. Frantically he struggled to free the lock from his belt, then he dropped his pistols and shot pouch. When he surfaced the third time his lungs seemed about to burst.

Too weak to swim, he kicked feebly. But his buckskin shirt, full of water, pulled his face under. Then his head bumped something hard and a voice hailed him. It was Reed Gibson in another skiff. "Give me your hand, Jim! I'll haul you in."

Somehow Reed hoisted him over the side. Exhausted, Jim flopped on the bottom, and Reed leaned into the oars, rowing toward the distant keelboats. They had escaped, for the moment. But back on the beach the Rees, with hideous shrieks of victory, were scalping and hacking up their slain comrades. And scores of other Rees were swimming across the river to intercept them.

Jim heard a rifle shot and Reed clasped both hands over his stomach. "Oh, Jim, I'm hit!" he gasped. "Mortal bad." With a groan he pitched forward and the skiff drifted out of control.

As Jim knelt over him to examine the wound the

boat gave a violent lurch. An Indian swimmer, knife between his teeth, was pulling himself up over the bow. Jim grabbed an oar and swung. Wood crunched against bone and the Ree sank without a sound.

"I'm not going to make it," Reed mumbled. "Promise me, Jim, you'll write my people back home in Virginia, tell them how I died."

"Sure, Reed. But you'll be all right." Stroking with all his might, Jim rowed for the far shore.

4. INDIANS AND GRIZZLIES

A BEND of the Missouri concealed the village
and the keelboats. Jim helped Reed out of the skiff,
left him hidden in the brush and crawled up the bank
to reconnoiter. As he stepped into the open his blood
froze. With a war whoop three Rees broke from the
timber and sprinted toward him, a hundred yards
away.

No chance to hide himself. He'd lost his weapons
and the Rees were armed with bows and tomahawks.
His one hope to save the helpless Reed was to decoy
them away, then maybe later he could circle back.
Jim turned and ran for his life.

Flat empty prairie spread for miles, but one small
rise loomed far off to the east. Legs churning, arms
pumping, he lowered his head and made for that.

His moccasins slapped the wet turf and air whistled in and out of his lungs. He remembered another trapper, John Colter, who once had outrun a whole tribe of Blackfeet. Colter had been stripped naked first; at least Jim had his clothes. To these Indians the footrace was a cruel and bloody game.

Risking a glance over one shoulder, he saw that his three pursuers had spread out. The one in the middle was gaining but the other two had fallen back. In desperation Jim put forth a fresh burst of speed, ran on and on. The low rise seemed no closer. His heart hammered in his chest. Lights swam before his eyes. But he kept pounding along on wobbly legs.

And then abruptly he topped the ridge. No Indians in sight. Below him was a foot-deep hollow in the prairie, screened by grass. He tumbled into it. Scarcely daring to breathe, he lay motionless.

Soon the three Rees ran past his hole. They stopped, so close he could smell their grease-smeared bodies, made a brief search and hurried on. Miraculously, they had missed him. Jim watched them halt again, on a rise half a mile away. Grinning with relief, he got to his feet and made a low mocking bow. Then he ran in the opposite direction, back toward the river.

As he scrambled down the bank the two keelboats swung around a bend and a shout went up. General Ashley was the first to greet him. "Jim, praise God! We thought you'd gone under."

"Almost did, General," Jim said. "I'm going back to hunt for Reed Gibson."

"We already found him." Ashley shook his head. "Poor lad, he's sinking fast."

His head in Jim's lap, Reed died without regaining consciousness, and John Gardner soon after. In all, thirteen trappers were dead and eleven wounded, a third of the expedition. It was the worst disaster the fur trade had suffered in its history. Jim never forgot this harsh lesson.

Hundreds of Rees still lurked along the bank, so the boats proceeded downriver to an island. Here the weary heartsick trappers landed and buried their dead. Some blamed the general, others cursed the boatmen for failing to come to their rescue. But they all knew that, except for Jim's coolness under fire, many more would have died. Greenhorn no longer, today he'd become a real mountain man.

As they gathered around the graves he said to Jed Smith, "Reed Gibson saved my life. Say a prayer for him, Jed."

"I'm no preacher, Jim."

"No matter, you're a godly man, and our souls have been sore tried this day. I want to tell Reed's family that he had a decent burial."

After the service he and Jed and Ashley held a war council. The general was all for fighting back up the river, right past the Ree villages. But the *voyageurs* refused to man the boats. They'd had enough of Indians. Without horses or boats, the brigade could not go on.

"We've got to punish those Rees, sir," Jim insisted. "Or no white man will be safe along the Missouri again."

Ashley agreed. It was decided to remove the wounded downriver and send out messengers for reinforcements. During the weeks of waiting Jim kept the camp supplied with fresh meat. Each day they expected a Ree raid, but none came. Then late in June twenty more trappers arrived from the Yellowstone, led by the general's partner, Andrew Henry, and young Jim Bridger.

Shortly afterward Colonel Leavenworth pushed upriver from Fort Atkinson with six companies of Army infantry, and three small cannon. Last to arrive was a band of trappers from the Missouri Fur Company. In this common crisis rival firms had to join forces. But the sight that made Jim's eyes pop was a band of Sioux, six hundred strong, who rode in to help defeat the Rees.

Mounted on splendid ponies, decked out in feathered war bonnets and all their battle finery, the Sioux were a brilliant spectacle. For two days they feasted and danced and made ready to fight. Meanwhile Leavenworth organized his command into what he called the Missouri Legion and gave a rousing speech. The blood of the trappers and traders must be avenged, he stated, until peace was restored in the land.

"Has he ever fought Indians before?" Jim asked.

"Not him," Black Harris said. "He's a spit an' polish so'jer. Them Sioux'll do whatever strikes their heathen fancy."

"Dangdest rag-tag Army I ever seed," Jim Bridger put in. "More Injuns than white."

At last the Missouri Legion advanced to the attack. As they neared the Ree stronghold the Sioux galloped ahead, leaving the trappers to follow on foot. At the sight of their ancient foes, the Rees burst from their stockade. Brave met brave in hand-to-hand combat as the savage battle raged along the river bank. It was a scene of wildest pandemonium—guns booming, Indians whooping, riderless horses trampling over the cornfields. Jim ran up through the dust and opened fire.

Just one shot at Gray Eyes or Little Soldier, he thought grimly, to pay them back for Reed Gibson.

But the Rees abruptly broke off. They retreated behind the barricade, leaving their dead behind. The blood-crazed Sioux dragged the corpses up and down the battleground and screamed abuse, daring their enemies to come out and renew the fight. Then the Army brought up their howitzers and poured cannon-balls into the enclosure. Sure that they could breach the walls in a mass charge, Jim and his men waited impatiently for a chance to avenge their friends.

But the chance never came. Colonel Leavenworth called off the bombardment and made plans for a siege. For two days he delayed and hesitated, while the trappers grew more disgusted. At length the Sioux became disgusted too. They couldn't understand this kind of warfare. They'd come to show off their valor, to take scalps and count coups, not to sit around till the enemy gave up and quit. In a huff they packed up their tepees and disappeared.

"That colonel made a big mistake," Cutnose said. "Now the Sioux think we're scared old women. After this they'll laugh at the Army."

Jim agreed. The white man had lost face among

all the plains tribes. On the fourth day Little Soldier came out to parley. Gray Eyes had been killed by cannon fire, he said. The Rees wished to sue for peace. The white medicine was too strong. The Rees spoke with a straight tongue and hereafter their hearts would be good. Tomorrow, Little Soldier promised, they would come out to surrender.

But Jim spoke his mind. The Ree chiefs had made a similar promise two months ago, then launched their treacherous attack. "It's a trick, Colonel. He's playing for time."

"I'm in command, sir," Leavenworth snapped. "Tomorrow we'll sign a treaty."

No smoke rose from village cook fires at daybreak. No squaws wailed out their grief behind the log walls. The stockade was silent as a grave. Creeping up to the gate, Jim found it deserted. During the night every single Ree—man, woman and child—had sneaked out under the noses of the Army guards and escaped.

"Well, the war's over," Ashley said. "But what a miserable showing we made."

Jim nodded. True, they had reopened the river to travel. But now the embittered Rees were scattered across Dakota, burning for revenge. No trapper would be safe for years to come.

48

Still in need of horses, Ashley took the expedition back downriver to Fort Kiowa, where he secured a few pack animals and split his men for the fall hunt. The larger group would return to the Yellowstone. The second brigade, of eleven men, including Jim, Jed Smith, Bill Sublette, Tom Fitzpatrick, Black Harris and Cutnose, was to strike west into a region never trapped before.

"We have to find new beaver streams," the general said. "And some way to bring those furs to market. There may be a low pass through the Rockies."

Years before, an exploring party had reported such a pass. But no white man had seen it since. If Jim's group found a practical route into virgin beaver country they were to send work back to Ashley. He would meet them somewhere in the mountains two years hence. They were to be the spearhead of the Rocky Mountain Fur Company. The general himself had to return to St. Louis to buy supplies and recruit more men.

"I'm counting on you, Jim," he said. "Good luck and God bless you all."

In blazing September heat Jim's little band set out. On them depended the success or failure of the company, for this past summer of disaster had plunged

49

the firm deep in debt. And Jim hadn't caught one beaver yet. He'd been too busy fighting Indians.

The country was dry and arid but everything about it fascinated him. With the eye of a one-time farmer he studied the soil, made notes about the climate, plants and animals they saw. Bill Sublette joshed him about this. "What you aim to do, Jim? Survey this desert into townships and sell lots?"

"The land is good for grazing livestock," Jim said. "And with water this soil will raise almost any crop."

"Who'd want to farm out here? Injuns, maybe?"

Jim grinned. Most Americans and the Government in far-off Washington thought of all this land beyond the Missouri as worthless barren desert, fit only for the red man. But he remembered how Ohio and Indiana once had been wilderness too. "Go ahead and laugh, Bill. But I saw the Ohio Valley fill up. We'll see it here someday. Settlers crowding in to take up good cheap land."

Bill shook his head. Americans plowing up empty prairie? Jim was full of queer notions. But nobody laughed at this quiet rawhide Virginian, who read poetry aloud around the campfire and composed his own verses.

Then the Indian guide deserted. Lost and collapsing from thirst in the heat, the brigade staggered on.

Jim scouted ahead and found a waterhole, led the others to safety. They crossed a desolate badlands and came to a Sioux hunting camp, where they traded for more horses. Anxious to reach the mountains before first snowfall, they hurried toward Absaroka, the Crow country of western Wyoming, where they hoped to learn of the mysterious pass.

Jim had killed many a bear, but he had never seen a dreaded grizzly of the Far West. These great beasts grew to a length of nine feet, sometimes weighed as much as an ox, and would attack a man. Swift and ferocious and tremendously powerful, they were feared by trapper and Indian alike, especially a female with a cub.

Tramping single file through the Black Hills one afternoon, the column sighted movement in the brush. "Grizzly bar!" the cry went up. Horses caught the scent and bolted in terror. In the lead, Jim and Jed Smith ran to a clearing. With a growl a huge female silvertip sprang on Jed and grabbed his head between her terrible jaws.

Jim raised his rifle, but could not shoot for fear of hitting Jed. The grizzly hurled Jed to the ground and leaped on him again. Her teeth snapped shut on his ball pouch, crunching and grinding. Then Jim got in his shot. The bear went down with a bullet through her heart. They gathered around Jed and Black Harris muttered, "Gar, he's done for, poor Jed."

Jim knelt down. Jed was still conscious, but covered with blood. The bear had torn his scalp and almost ripped off one ear. "Water!" Jim ordered.

With some shirting he used for rifle patches, he washed Jed's wounds. Then he got a needle and thread from his kit and sewed up the mangled flesh as best he could. Staring up at Jim, Jed gritted his teeth. "Now, sew on my ear," he whispered.

"I can't, Jed. I just can't."

"You must, Jim."

Jim knew the agony this would be for his friend. But somehow he stitched the ear back in place. Jed didn't faint once. The brigade had no medicine, not even whisky to dull the pain. The others were sure Jed would die. But Jim remembered a home remedy his mother had taught him. Mixing a poultice of sugar and soap, he applied it to Jed's wounds. Within ten days Jed was up and around again, although badly scarred.

"You saved my life, Jim," he said. "Where did you learn to doctor like that?"

Embarrassed, Jim told him, "On a farm you learn how to take care of your animals."

The trappers laughed. They had another yarn to

spin around their campfires. That Jim Clyman could do anything. Hunt and fight, write poetry, outrun an Injun, down a grizzly bear. Or hemstitch a man's ear back onto his head.

5. TRAPPER AND EXPLORER

Wɪᴛʜɪɴ a few days the brigade came upon the first fur sign. Jim's education in the art of catching beaver now began, under the sharp eye of Black Harris. "Idee is to drown the critter," Black explained. "If he crawls out on land he'll chaw off his leg an' git away."

A full-grown beaver sometimes weighed as much as forty pounds, so a heavy trap was required to hold the animal. Black located the underwater entrance to a den, then waded into the stream and set his trap a few inches below the surface. He secured it with a chain, which he attached to an iron stake driven deep into the muddy bottom. Above the trap he tied some "bait," a twig smeared with scent from beaver castor glands. Next he fastened a six-foot length of stick, a float, to the chain, so that if the trap did pull loose he could still find his catch.

The final step was to wade ashore, some distance from the set, and sprinkle water along the bank to remove every trace of human scent. By the end of that first day Jim's legs ached from hours in an icy creek. But next morning he was rewarded by finding three fine beaver in his traps. "Now we'll have us some beaver tail," Black said. "Best eatin' meat in the mountings."

Black then showed him how to skin an animal, scrape the fat off the underside, and stretch its pelt on a willow frame. Fifty of these, pressed fur-side down into a bale, would be worth about three hundred dollars. The skin, called a "plew," was at its prime in fall or spring. Summer plews were coarser, therefore less valuable. During the winter months all streams froze up solid. This cycle of nature was the trapper's calendar.

After a fair catch the little band pushed on through freezing weather to the Wind River and to the main Crow encampment. Here, for the first time, Jim stood in the shadow of the Rockies, the snow-capped spine of North America. With awe he stared up at the jagged peaks. After a journey of eight dangerous and adventure-packed months he had reached the mountains at last.

The Crows, like the Sioux, were wanderers, a fierce warlike people, expert hunters and horsemen who followed the buffalo migrations. Because they were always at war with their neighbors, especially the powerful Blackfeet to the north, they welcomed the Americans as allies. Also, these white men were friends of Cutnose, an adopted Crow chief. So Jim moved into the warm comfort of an elkhide tepee for the winter.

One day in late November a crier ran through the village shouting out some news. Black poked his head through the flap. "Grab yore rifle, Jim. We're goin' on a buffler surround!"

A big herd had been sighted and the whole camp hurried out to take part in the hunt. Jim joined the fastest Crow riders on their fleet ponies. They rode forward, keeping downwind from the buffalo, who have a keen sense of smell, and circled around behind. Finally in position, they made a sudden uproar, firing rifles and pistols, whooping and waving blankets. The frightened herd broke into a gallop and the pursuers stampeded it down a narrow valley.

The other Crows, hidden on either side, opened fire as the thundering herd poured through this gap.

Those without guns dropped buffalo with bows and spears and chased down the stragglers on foot. Jim shot a big bull and reloaded on the run. He ran until the horse was exhausted, downing nine more buffalo. When he returned to camp, squaws were busy cutting up the carcasses, slicing off steaks to broil, while the braves gobbled down liver and intestines and raw meat. In an hour or so several hundred buffalo had been killed, enough to feed the camp for months.

At the feast that night the Crows eyed Jim with new respect. They were glad to have such a mighty hunter as their winter guest.

In turn Jim entered into Indian life with full zest. They taught him how to tan hides, make moccasins and beadwork, many other crafts. He came to admire these people, who bathed each morning even when they had to chop holes in the ice, and who taught their young to ride from infancy. The days passed pleasantly. But in February a thaw set in. It was time to push on again, search for a pass through the Rockies and the beaver streams beyond.

But Cutnose was no longer around to interpret. He'd quit the brigade and gone off to another camp. In vain Jim struggled to make the chief understand what he wanted. The old man only shook his head. So Jim unrolled a buffalo robe and heaped up mounds of dirt and rock on it to represent mountains. Grinning and nodding now, the chief rearranged Jim's "map."

"That hollow he made to the south," Jim said, "must be a pass. The South Pass."

"And that wavy line beyond it," Jed Smith put in, "the one he calls 'Seeds-kee-dee,' must be the Green River we've heard about."

"If it's there," Jim said, "we'll find it."

So they said good-by to their hosts and, following the chief's directions, struck off to the south. But a new storm swept down with galelike fury. Game was scarce and their food supply soon ran out. Men and horses grew weak from hunger and the bitter cold. Leaving the others in camp one afternoon, Jim and Bill Sublette rode out to hunt. Snowdrifts were so deep they took turns tramping out a path for their animals.

Later they sighted three gaunt buffalo. Crawling across the ice on his stomach, Jim wounded one with his rifle, then finished it off with his knife. He and Bill gathered what fuel there was—a few handfuls of sagebrush—made a fire and cooked some of the meat. With night coming on they crawled under their one robe and huddled together for warmth.

A fierce wind blew out the fire and scattered the

embers. More snow began to fall. Jim had never known such deadly cold, that struck to the bone. "We'll freeze to death without a fire," he said.

"I'm plumb froze now," Bill said. "Must be forty below zero."

"I'll go find some brush," Jim told him. "You stay here under the robe. Keep your hands warm so you can strike a light when I get back."

But when he returned with more sage neither man could strike a spark from their flint and steel. Their hands were too numb and stiff. Desperate now, they stamped about in the darkness to keep their blood circulating. Wind howled and shrieked about them. Rapidly Bill grew weaker. When dawn finally crept over the bleak frozen wasteland, Jim knew he had to get Bill down to shelter or his friend would perish.

He saddled up and helped Bill mount, then set out for a distant patch of timber, leading the horses on foot. It took him four hours to struggle four miles, followed by several starving wolves. Among the trees he found an abandoned Indian lodge and plenty of dry wood and tinder. He got a fire started, carried Bill inside, then rubbed him with snow and forced him to chew some raw meat. With food and warmth Bill quickly revived.

Afterwards Bill didn't put his gratitude in words.

59

Out in the wilderness each man depended on the other. Bill Sublette would have done as much for Jim.

Rejoining the brigade next day, they crossed to a river named the Sweetwater. Storm followed storm. During one thirty-six-hour blizzard they had to burrow under their robes like badgers in a den. No man could stand erect in the furious winds. But at last the weather cleared. They shot mountain sheep and gathered cottonwood bark for the horses. Caching a quantity of gunpowder and lead under the rocks, where they hoped no Indians would find and loot it, the men broke camp and climbed toward the headwaters.

This country was the most desolate yet—barren hills and windswept ridges. They ran out of food again and had to butcher a horse. The only water to drink was melted snow. All the world seemed locked in winter's icy grip. But nobody talked of turning back. They had gone through too many hardships to give up now.

On the sixth day they topped out on a high plain and the sun broke through the clouds. Jim stopped beside a stream whose course was marked by brush. He peered across the flat dreary expanse and squinted up at the sun. "Boys, I think this is it," he said in a voice of rising excitement. "The continental divide!"

"Watcha mean, Jim?"

"The pass. The South Pass we've been looking for. We've reached the top."

"Looks like any other cussed rock pile to me," grumbled Joe Stone.

"Maybe," Jim said. "But look at that creek. It flows west, downhill, toward the sun. If you threw a stick in, it'd float clear to the Pacific."

Jed Smith grinned. Bill Sublette whacked him on the back. "You done it, Jim! You and your crazy map. We're over the hump. Wagh!"

None of them realized the true significance of that March day of 1824. They were too cold and hungry and tired to care. But Jim and his band had discovered a gateway through the Rockies, a route that was to affect the history of the United States.

Several days later they reached a large river which could be only the Green. Here the party divided, agreeing to meet back at the powder cache by June 15. Jed and six men turned south, while Jim, Tom Fitzpatrick and two others went north. Soon flocks of geese were seen winging north and the river ice broke up. Spring had arrived. Jim and his three companions eagerly set out their traps.

The upper Green and its tributaries proved fabulously rich in beaver. Day by day the furs piled up.

At this rate, Tom joked, they'd all be millionaires in one season. Then a band of some forty Snake Indians visited their little camp.

The Snake tribe was not hostile toward whites, like the Rees and Blackfeet, but they had a reputation as thieves. Under the circumstances Jim had no choice but to try and get along with them. He ordered his men to give all their beaver meat to the Indians as a gift. Delighted by this generosity, the Snakes vowed eternal friendship for their paleface brothers. But one night they stole every horse and disappeared.

Jim accepted this bitter loss resignedly. It was one of the perils of a trapper's life. But he swore never to be so careless again. They buried their peltries and plodded back downriver on foot. A thousand miles beyond the nearest settlement, they had little hope of buying more horses from some other tribe.

About noon the following day they rounded a point and came face to face with six mounted Snakes. On their horses! Instantly Jim leveled his rifle. Cowed by four grim, heavily armed Americans, the Indians surrendered and led the way to a nearby village, where they gave up the rest of the stolen stock. A great stroke of luck, Jim thought. But one horse still was missing, his favorite gray.

He knew he must make an example. If he showed

any softness they would mistake it for cowardice and rob him again. Snatching up a rope, he tied a loop and pulled it tight around the leader's neck. "Where is the gray one?" he demanded, and made the sign of a horse.

The terrified Snake gasped out an order. Another Indian darted into the brush and led out the missing horse. "Blasted varmints!" Francis Branch rumbled. "Rub him out, Jim. Only good Injun's a dead Injun."

Many trappers felt that way. They had seen their friends killed, lost their furs and traps and all their goods to Indians. But Jim could see the Indian side too. The Indians had lived in this land for centuries and looked upon it as their home. They resented and feared the white invaders. "No need of that," he said. "We got what we came for."

After distributing presents of tobacco, to ease the pride of the Snakes, he rode off to dig up his furs. By a show of firmness, without shedding a drop of blood, he had turned disaster into victory. "That was smart, Jim," Tom told him. "The Snakes'll know better than to jump us next time."

Jim smiled. Some day, he hoped, a man would be able to cross this country without dreading an ambush or an arrow in the back. Indian and white must learn to live side by side in peace. But that might be years in the future. "One sure thing, Tom," he said. "The smartest Indian fighter is the one who fights the least. He heads off trouble before it starts."

They crossed back over South Pass to the meeting point on the Sweetwater, but there was no sign of the other party. Jim opened the cache and, finding their powder damp, spread it out in the sun to dry. "While we're waiting," he told his men, "I might as well push ahead, see if we can float our furs down in bullboats. This river must empty into the Missouri."

"Good idea," Tom agreed. "A lot easier than packing them on horses."

"I'll be back in a few days," Jim said, and rode off alone.

The Sweetwater was swift and too shallow for even a bullboat, a round bowl-shaped craft the trappers made by sewing buffalo skins over a willow framework. But Jim kept on for three days, hoping to find deep water. As Tom had said, a navigable outlet would mean they could ship their furs all the way to General Ashley in St. Louis. At the junction of a larger stream he decided to make camp before exploring any farther.

Down among a grove of willows, he was about to light his fire when he heard voices. Always cautious in Indian country, he tied a strip of rawhide around his horse's muzzle so that it couldn't whinny and give him away. Then he crawled to the river bank and peered out.

A party of Indians painted for war rode up the opposite bank. Twenty-two, Jim counted. Rees! Then his heart sank. In the lead was his old enemy, the Ree chief, Little Soldier.

6. A DANGEROUS TREK

To HIS dismay the Rees made camp directly across the river. If one of them happened to cross over, his footprints would be discovered. He must confuse the trail he had left. Jim crawled out of the trees and, concealed by a small bluff, walked backwards for half a mile across the sand. Any second the Indians might appear. But he reached a rocky ridge, followed this back to the river and swam across. From a high point he could observe the rear of the Ree camp.

Except for an accident they might never have suspected that a white man was hiding nearby. But two ponies broke away from the herd, swam across the river, and waded out near Jim's camp. A warrior sent to bring them back found Jim's horse among the willows. He let out a whoop and the hunt was on. The whole war party spread out to search. From his hole in the rocks Jim watched Little Soldier puzzle over the row of footprints in the sand. It was this trick which saved him.

The Rees hunted through the night, aided by bright moonlight. Next morning they broke camp and moved upriver, still looking for the elusive paleface who somehow had fooled their best trackers.

For a long while Jim didn't dare move, but finally thirst drove him down to the river bank. He was drinking when a second band of Rees filed out of the timber. Jim flattened in the brush. For some while they searched back and forth, then rode on in the opposite direction from the first war party. Jim crept back to his hole.

His situation was desperate. He had only eleven bullets left in his shot pouch and very few rations. He was afoot in strange country, surrounded by enemies lusting to catch and torture him. The only possible help was far away—three trappers who would be hard pressed to save their own lives.

For twelve days he hid in the rocks, while Indians camped and hunted all around him. At night he sneaked out for water. By now he knew that either his friends had given him up for lost, or were dead themselves. Following the river, he struck out for Fort Atkinson on the Missouri, six hundred miles to the east.

Risking a shot, he killed a buffalo and dried as much meat as he could carry. Twice during the next week he saw Ree hunting parties in the distance and had to hide. Farther downriver he spied a herd of wild horses. Perhaps he could capture one to ride. Shooting another buffalo, he cut up its hide and made a halter. Then he concealed himself and waited for the horses to return to water.

A handsome black stallion led the herd down the bank. Jim took careful aim. His hope was to stun the horse by a "crease" shot along the neck without wounding the animal, a difficult feat of marksmanship. His rifle boomed, the stallion flung up its head and fell over dead. Jim had shot an inch too low. With only eight bullets left, he stumbled along on his lonely nightmare journey.

Later he came upon the travois marks—made by the dragging lodge poles—of an Indian village on the move. Suddenly several braves sprang out of the bushes in his path. By their markings he recognized them as Pawnees, an unpredictable plains tribe whom no white man trusted. Their leader flourished a knife and thrust the blade against Jim's chest.

A Dangerous Trek

Jim stood motionless, staring back into the cruel eyes. "Never let an Indian know you're scared!" His lesson from the War of 1812 flashed through his mind. If he flinched now they would kill him. Impressed by this show of bravery, the Pawnee stepped back. The others stripped Jim of his belongings—rifle, shot pouch, flint and steel. A tall Indian on a horse motioned him to follow, led him to the village and into a lodge.

Jim slept very little that night, convinced he would be dead by morning. Outside the chiefs harangued each other and argued his fate. At daybreak the tall Pawnee returned, motioned Jim to follow again. Two miles out on the prairie, beyond the sight of the village, he told Jim in sign language he must escape before the others decided to kill him.

But one favor Jim must grant first. The Indian wanted Jim's hair, which hadn't been cut since he left St. Louis seventeen months before. Jim couldn't help but grin. A fair exchange—his hair for his life. Sometimes an Indian had a funny whim like this. Maybe it was a form of kindness. So the Pawnee hacked off Jim's flowing locks, gave him a little parched corn and rode away.

Scarcely able to believe his luck, Jim left the river.

Too many Indians hunted along its banks. Next time they might lift his scalp as well as his hair.

Soon the corn was gone. He ate roots and berries, whatever he could find. Once he stumbled across two fighting badgers and killed them with a buffalo bone. Their meat kept up his strength a few more days. Constant rains chilled him to the marrow and mosquitoes, breeding in the buffalo wallows, plagued him night and day. His buckskins, worn to tatters, hung loose on his gaunt frame.

He swam so many rivers he lost count. Weak and sick and half delirious, he blundered onto a trail. Not far ahead the log walls of a stockade loomed up. Tears stung his eyes as he stared at Old Glory rippling on the flagpole. Fort Atkinson! Jim was so overcome with feeling he fainted in the grass.

He hadn't seen a white man in three months. Without a compass, guided by his frontiersman's unerring instinct, he had crossed hundreds of miles of country unknown to him. Starving, dodging hostile Indians all the while, he had hit his target dead center.

Barely able to walk, he hobbled through the gate. An astounded officer gaped at this scarecrow figure, then took him to Colonel Leavenworth, his old commander in the Ree campaign. Leavenworth welcomed him hospitably, and after a few days Jim felt fit and ready to go again. Then three more emaciated trappers limped into the fort. Jim rubbed his eyes. It couldn't be! Tom Fitzpatrick, Francis Branch and Joe Stone, whom he'd left on the Sweetwater back in June.

"Tom!" he exclaimed. "I never thought to see you three alive again."

Tom gripped his hand. "Same to you, Jim. You look like a ghost from the grave."

That night the four friends had a gala reunion and Tom related their story. After finding Jim's camp among so much Indian sign, they assumed he must have been slain. Then Jed Smith arrived with his spring hunt and returned to the mountains, leaving Tom to transport all the furs to St. Louis. Tom, Branch and Stone had made a bullboat and started down the river but were overturned in the rapids. They managed to save and cache the fur packs, but two of their rifles and all their supplies were lost. Like Jim, they had suffered much in their long walk back to civilization.

"Well, we all made it," Tom said. "The luck of the Irish."

"More like a miracle, Tom," Jim said. "I prayed to God every night out there." This ordeal had proved one thing. There was no navigable river flowing from the Rockies into the Missouri. They would have to transport their furs and supplies by horse. "Now we'll send word to General Ashley that we've found a pass through the mountains, and good rich beaver streams. He'll be anxious."

"What about those furs I buried?" Tom asked. "They're worth a fortune."

"I'll go back for them, before the Indians discover that cache and rob it."

"You're in no shape to travel, Jim," Tom protested. "After what you've been through."

"A year's sweat and grief's gone into those furs," Jim said. "Without 'em the company may go under, financially, and us with it."

Tom grinned. "You stubborn mule. All right, I'll go too. If it kills us both."

Swiftly Jim and Tom rounded up some horses and a small, heavily armed party. Traveling at top speed, they retraced within days the route that had taken them many painful weeks a short time before. No Indians bothered them. Far up the Sweetwater, Tom led the way to a huge rock on which he'd carved his name. "We were wrecked near here on the Fouth of July," he explained, "so I named it Independence Rock."

The cache was untouched. They dug up the furs,

loaded them on pack horses and hurried back to Fort Atkinson, completing a remarkable round-trip journey of twelve hundred miles in one month. Years passed before Jim was to know that, in his epic escape from the Rees, he had blazed part of the famous Oregon Trail.

A worried General Ashley was waiting at the fort. He had received Jim's letter in St. Louis and, on the strength of that news, had organized a new expedition to trap beyond the Rockies. This time Ashley was going along himself. "I want you to guide me, Jim," he said. "Through that pass you boys found."

Jim exchanged a look with Tom. Turn right around and go back? A fourth trip up the Sweetwater in less than six months? Then Jim chuckled. "It won't be easy, General. Not in winter. But Tom and I can lead you through that country blindfolded now."

Ashley was delighted with the furs. The money they would bring meant the company could stay in business at least one more year. But most of his news was bad. Hugh Glass had been almost killed by a grizzly. So many disasters had befallen Ashley's partner, Andrew Henry, that he was quitting the fur trade for good. The Blackfeet had massacred fifteen trappers and driven out the rest. The Min-

73

netarees and even the Crows had been stealing horses and traps and furs. All the upper Missouri tribes seemed to be on the warpath.

Jim's eyes glowed. He knew the dangers of that country. But nothing could scare him out now. "How soon do we leave, sir?"

"The sooner the better," Ashley told him. "If we don't make a good haul this next year, I'm licked too."

The general had recruited twenty-five men, all new to the mountains, and bought dozens of horses to carry supplies and trade goods to his trappers far out in the field. On November 3 the long caravan got under way, striking west across the Nebraska prairies. As Jim had predicted, it was a hard cold trip. Storms howled down, covering the ground with two feet of snow. The men were rationed to half a pint of flour a day, made into gruel. Some days they covered only a few miles or could not travel at all.

Jim led them off his old trail to the Platte River, where they found game and fuel and grass for their horses. The general favored taking the shortest route, but Jim shook his head, remembering his own bitter experience on the Sweetwater last winter. The men would freeze without firewood. They must locate some other route, close to trees and brush.

A Dangerous Trek

The day after Christmas a blizzard struck. Many horses died. The expedition could advance only by following a path that a buffalo herd had trampled out. But early in February they reached the foot of the Rockies and camped below the mighty Front Range. Then five Pawnees rode in with an alarming report. The Pawnees, eager to trade, warned that a war party of one hundred Rees was wintering not far to the south. Also hostile Arapahos and Kiowas were in the vicinity.

The men stood guard night and day in shifts. For three weeks they waited for the weather to clear, fearful of an attack. Fortunately, thanks to Jim's foresight, they had ample wood to burn. At last they turned west again, straight into the mountains. Jim plowed ahead through deep drifts, blazing a trail. After days of struggle he led the party down into the plains of Wyoming. No white man had crossed the Front Range before: Jim Clyman had done it in midwinter.

Here was game in abundance, and beaver streams. Their troubles seemed over. But one day Jim and Tom returned from trapping to find the camp in an uproar. Indians had run off seventeen of the remaining horses. Jim took eight men and rode in pursuit. The trail led to a rocky canyon and vanished. "Our friends the Crows," Tom said bitterly. "The slickest horse thieves born."

Jim nodded. The Crows had too long a start. This never would have happened if he'd been in camp. Somebody had been careless. "We were greenhorns too last year, Tom," he said. "They'll learn."

The general hoped to cross South Pass. But now, short of pack animals, the men had to carry loads on their backs. So once again Jim scouted ahead for some shorter routes. He found a low saddle through the continental divide, one that a transcontinental railroad uses today, and guided the heavily burdened trappers down the Pacific watershed. Late in April he stood once again on the banks of Green River, heart of a beaver empire.

Ten months had passed since he last saw the Green. Now an idea formed in his mind. Since the Sweetwater and Platte had proved unnavigable, why not explore this great river? It might be a deep-water outlet, leading into the Gulf of Mexico, or even the far Pacific. Such a route, if one existed, would save the company money and horses and human lives.

But General Ashley had other plans for him. "I'm sorry, Jim," he said. "I know you have an itch to explore new country. But you're my best trapper. I need you too badly here."

"Send somebody, General. No trapper, no white man, has ever been down the Green."

"You're right," Ashley said. "But as head of the company I think I'd better go myself."

Jim swallowed his disappointment. He made two bullboats, calking the seams with a mixture of ashes and buffalo tallow so they would be watertight. Then the expedition split into four groups, one to explore and three to trap. Ashley and his band shoved off down the river. Jim, in charge of three greenhorns, turned the opposite direction—north. All agreed to meet at the mouth of a tributary three months thence.

7. THE GREAT BASIN

THE most efficient method of trapping a beaver stream was to work in small bands of two to five men. For that same reason it was highly dangerous—Indians seldom attacked a large band of trappers, although they might steal horses any time. Well aware of this, Jim took every precaution, in camp and on the trap line. For many weeks they found no Indian sign at all.

His three men—the French-Canadian Pierre LaBarge, a mulatto named Jim Beckwourth, and young Dan Glover—made a fine spring hunt. They moved slowly up the Green and turned west on a large creek. But one morning a party of seventeen Arapaho bucks, the first Jim had seen, rode into camp. Like many other western tribes, the Arapahos were sometimes hostile, sometimes friendly, depending on their mood and the odds against them.

Jim's policy had worked with the Snakes last year, in almost the same circumstances. He told his men, "Dan, break out some of that trade tobacco. Maybe this bunch is peaceful. And Pierre, give them that leftover beaver meat. You, Jim, keep that chief covered with your rifle every second."

In the universal sign language the Arapahos explained that they were here to hunt. They accepted the gifts and made camp a short way up the creek. "Don't smell right to me," Jim Beckwourth said. "If they came to hunt why ain't they down in buffalo country?"

"Maybe we'd best pull our traps and slip off somewhere tonight," Dan Glover said. "Plenty of other good cricks."

"No, they'd follow us, once we ran," Jim said. "Catch us, too, because we can't travel fast with all this fur. We have to face 'em out."

He picketed their horses in a clearing beside camp. During the day two men stood guard while the other two trapped. At night each of the four took a two-hour turn at guard duty. The constant strain, the nights of broken sleep, wore them down. But the Indians showed no inclination to move on. A dozen or so always skulked about through the trees.

On the fourth night Jim told his men, "Tomorrow

we'll shift camp. We've cleaned out the beaver on this stream anyway. Pierre, you stand first watch. I'll relieve you at midnight."

LaBarge stepped off into the darkness with his rifle and the others stretched out around the fire. Afterward Jim never knew whether the French-Canadian fell asleep at his post. But a blood-chilling whoop wakened him. Grabbing up his rifle, Jim jumped to his feet. A musket roared. The ball ripped his fur capote off his head. He fired back at the muzzle flash and yelled to his men, "Pour it to 'em, boys!"

By starlight he saw an Indian standing over La-Barge's prostrate form, swinging an ax. He drew his pistol and leaped forward, but the gun misfired. The Indian dropped his ax and ran. Pierre LaBarge was dead, his skull brutally smashed. Across the clearing Arapahos were hooting and howling, firing their muskets and bows into camp. Then, as Beckwourth and Glover fired back, they fled into the brush.

"Get some rocks," Jim ordered. "We'll fort up here."

They piled loose rock into a low breastwork along the creek bank and flattened behind it, where their rifles commanded the clearing. Not a sound broke the silence while they lay tense and unmoving. "Looks like we scared 'em off," Glover whispered.

Jim put a finger to his lips. Presently two stealthy figures crept from the trees toward the horse herd. Jim swung up his rifle and fired. One Indian went down, the other raced for cover. Hour after hour the three trappers waited, growing cold and cramped. Patience, Jim told himself. That was one more lesson a man had to learn in this hard country. He'd tried to avoid a fight, and failed. But perhaps he could save the other two men.

The sky was beginning to pale when Beckwourth nudged him and pointed. Not far up the creek several Arapahos were slipping out of the brush into the stream. "They're trying to sneak around behind us," Jim said.

Three rifles boomed. An Indian fell in the water. The others splashed back to the bank. Now Jim could hear sounds from their encampment, horses stomping and branches crackling. Then more silence. The sun was high overhead before he crawled out of the little fort and scouted up the creek. The Arapahos had struck their tepees and gone, taking their wounded. Three determined men had stood off seventeen.

They buried LaBarge beside the creek that still

bears his name, and hurried south to meet the other trappers. Word had spread throughout the mountains that General Ashley was on his way with supplies. Early in July scattered bands began to assemble on Henry's Fork of the Green, in what was to be the first annual rendezvous in the history of the American fur trade.

For Jim it was a time of happy reunion with old friends. They told each other of their adventures, and the wonders they had seen since last parting. Jed Smith had explored far to the north. Jim Bridger, on a bet, had discovered a huge mysterious lake of salt water in the desert. Ashley had had the hardest time of all, on his voyage down the Green.

"We'll never ship furs down that river," he told Jim. "It's full of terrible gorges and rapids. Twice I was overturned and nearly drowned. Finally I had to abandon the boats and come back on foot."

Bit by bit they pieced together their hard-won knowledge of the country, filling in blank spots. Each made his contribution. And Jim, who always listened more than he talked, stored away in his memory a map of every trail and pass and major stream for hundreds of miles around.

Next day the vital business of the rendezvous got under way. A hundred and twenty trappers were on hand—company employees like Jim, free trappers who worked for themselves, deserters from rival companies who came because Ashley had promised to pay the highest prices for their peltries. Many brought their Indian wives and children. Hundreds of friendly Indians, lured by the opportunity to trade, camped around the meadow. It was a noisy and colorful spectacle, a gala occasion after the months of danger and hardship.

General Ashley spread out his wares on the grass. The trappers, like hungry men at a feast, filed up one by one with their packs of beaver. First they bought necessities—rifles and pistols, new traps, powder and lead, axes and needles and awls. Then they bought such luxuries as tobacco, coffee and sugar to vary the monotony of their meat diet. Those who had some credit left bought finery for their women, beads, mirrors, bolts of cloth, bright blankets and vermilion paint.

Some plunged deep in debt. Others squandered a whole year's earnings on whisky, or lost it all gambling. The general charged high prices but nobody complained. Hadn't he run big risks to pack supplies so deep into Indian country? This saved the men a long hard trip back to some river fort.

Once the trading ended it was time to celebrate.

They organized sports and races, wrestling and shooting matches. They traded horses, played "hand" and other Indian betting games. At night around their fires they bragged and retold their favorite yarns, about Hugh Glass's fight with a grizzly bear, and how Jim Clyman had outrun the Rees. Jim smiled and sat back in the shadows. Already he'd become a legend among the mountain men.

All too soon rendezvous came to a close. Packing up their possibles bags, they made ready for another year of trapping. Next summer, Ashley announced, they would meet at a place known as Cache Valley, across the mountains to the west. Proudly he showed Jim his account book.

"We've taken in better than fifty thousand dollars' worth of beaver," he said. "More than I ever hoped. You boys kept the company from ruin."

Jim was pleased. He'd earned over a thousand dollars himself, and saved most of it. "You'll be going back to St. Louis now, General?"

"Leaving tomorrow," Ashley said. "Why don't you come along as guide, Jim? You've been away from civilization a long time."

Jim shook his head. Seven years had passed since he said good-by to his family back on the Ohio farm, although he received an occasional letter. He longed to see them. But all this mountain country was pulling at him like a magnet. "One of these days I'll go home. But not till I make a good stake."

The next few months went by quickly. Leading a small brigade, he headed west to see the strange lake Jim Bridger had described. It was a beautiful body of blue water, eight times as briny as the ocean, with dazzling white beds of salt crusted along its shores. When he waded in to swim, his body floated like a cork. Some day he was determined to explore it, but now he must press on to his fall hunt.

Jim and his men swung north and trapped along the Snake River of Idaho. Traveling in a wide circle, they reached the edge of Blackfoot territory and turned back with a big haul of furs, in time to join their comrades for the winter at Cache Valley. They built huts and laid in a supply of meat, and none too soon. By January, snow had piled up to a height of eight feet. Snowbound in his shelter, Jim spent many a pleasant day reading and writing and studying various Indian dialects, swapping information with his friends about the different tribes.

One night, under cover of a storm, a raiding party of Bannocks stole eighty of the company horses. At daybreak Jim organized forty men on snowshoes, including Tom Fitzpatrick and Jim Bridger, and set out in pursuit. The Bannocks, like their Snake cousins, were expert thieves, but not very warlike. Three nights later the trappers surprised them in their blankets and they gave up without a fight. Jim took back the eighty horses, and twenty extra ponies to teach the Bannocks a lesson, and returned to camp in triumph.

But early that spring tragedy struck down another of his men. As soon as the ground thawed he ordered caches dug. First the top sod was carefully removed in strips and set aside. After the hole was finished all excess dirt was piled on buffalo robes and dumped into a stream to be washed away. Then the sod was replaced and horses were led back and forth to trample out every trace of an excavation. Even so, Indians often spied out such hiding places and stole all the furs.

On this day the ground was soft from melting snow. John Marshall, a newcomer to the trade, jumped down to the bottom to shovel out some crumbling dirt. Too late Jim shouted a warning. With horror he saw the whole bank cave in. Marshall screamed and disappeared under tons of black earth. He smothered to death before they could dig him out.

Saddened by this loss, that night Jim wrote a letter to his brother John, which would be carried back to the settlements by the next supply caravan. For the first time he began to wonder about the hard life of a trapper. Was this the future he wanted for himself? What was his goal to be?

But his depression vanished in the excitement of preparing to explore Salt Lake. The Platte and Green rivers had proved unnavigable. According to some maps, however, a river led west from the lake all the way to California—the fabled Buenaventura. As he told Jed Smith, "If there's a river outlet anywhere on that lake I'm going to find it."

"That's quite a job," Jed said. "But think of the possibilities. A river emptying into the Pacific! I wish you luck, Jim."

With a dozen men he set out to ride around the north shore. Many still believed that the vast lake was actually an arm of the ocean. The country was desolate, bare of all vegetation except sage and salt grass, and water in the few springs was unfit to drink. Without feed the horses could travel no farther. Jim stopped and built a bullboat. "I'll keep three men with me," he said. "The rest of you carry on the trapping."

Black Harris, Louis Vasquez and Henry Fraeb volunteered. The four of them paddled off in their flimsy skin craft. Day after day the sun beat down

87

as they worked their way farther into the unknown desert. Not even Indians lived along these inhospitable shores. Food and water ran low. Millions of birds were nesting and the men ate their eggs, despite the somewhat bitter taste.

"By gar!" Vasquez growled. "I can never look a chicken in the eye after this."

On the south shore they found springs of fresh water and a large river pouring into the lake. But no river flowing *out*. Twenty-four days later they paddled back to their starting point and stepped ashore, gaunt and blackened by the sun. Despite his disappointment, Jim felt they had accomplished something. Until this year of 1826 no man had ever circumnavigated the Great Salt Lake.

Back at rendezvous that summer he compared notes with Jed Smith, who had been exploring to the northwest without success. "There isn't any Buenaventura," Jim said. "I'm convinced of that. We're wasting our time."

"No river to the Pacific, you mean?"

With a stick Jim sketched a map in the dirt. "All the rivers flow in, down from the mountains. This desert is like a great basin, catching their flow. No man knows yet how big it is."

"A great basin?" Jed nodded. "You were right

about South Pass, Jim. But not many people will believe you."

"They will someday, if they try to cross that desert out yonder. It's the road to California, Jed. The only road."

Jed didn't laugh. He was one of the very few who, like Jim, foresaw a day when thousands of their fellow Americans would be moving across this raw empty land. And Jim had never yet been wrong in his geography.

8. THE WANDERER

A<small>T</small> <small>THE</small> end of rendezvous General Ashley summoned Jim to his tent and revealed that he was quitting the fur trade. The past two years he had made so much profit, Ashley said, that he was selling out and running for governor of Missouri in the next election. Would Jim like to buy a part interest in the Rocky Mountain Fur Company?

"I'm anxious to leave the company in the best hands possible," the general said. "Nobody knows this business better than you, Jim. There's still lots of money to be made."

It was a tempting offer but Jim hesitated only a second. "Thank you, General," he said. "I'm flattered that you asked me. But I'm not a businessman at heart. As a partner I'd be tied down to details. I'd rather come and go as I please."

Ashley smiled. "I was afraid you'd turn me down. But think about it first."

Ever since Marshall's death in the cave-in Jim had given serious thought to leaving the mountains himself. His reasons were practical as well as personal. Back in 1823 his small brigade had been the only group of trappers in the Rockies. Now there were hundreds of competitors. Already the Snake River country was trapped out. Each year he had to hunt farther to find beaver. Each year the Indians grew more hostile and dangerous. One day soon, he felt sure, the fur supply would be exhausted.

"No, sir," he said. "I've made up my mind."

So three of his friends—Jed Smith, Bill Sublette and Davy Jackson—became the firm's new owners, or "big booshways," as the trappers called them. General Ashley made a farewell speech and rode off for St. Louis. With regret Jim watched his old employer go. It was this kindly, stubborn man who had given him his first real opportunity.

That fall he returned to his favorite trapping stream, the upper Green. But even here beaver were less plentiful than in other years. After wintering near the Salt Lake he made plans for his riskiest venture yet—a two-man expedition into the heart of the Blackfoot nation.

For several years no trapper had entered that region. It was impossible to parley or trade with the Blackfeet. The most feared and warlike tribe on the continent, they attacked all white men on sight. But their virgin rivers and creeks abounded in beaver. Two men might succeed, Jim reasoned, where a large band would be detected.

His friends advised against it. "You're crazy as a cuckoo," Black Harris told him. "Better pick your tombstone now."

Jim grinned. "If I can't die rich, Black, I might as well lose my hair. But before I go I'll write you an epitaph. How's this?

> *"Here lie the bones of Old Black Harris*
> *Who often traveled beyond the Far West*
> *And for the freedom of equal rights*
> *He crossed the snowy mountain heights.*
> *Was a free and easy kind of soul*
> *Especially when he had a belly full."*

The camp roared with laughter. From the trappers who asked to join him, Jim chose young Dan Glover. Dan had proved himself a cool hand in emergencies since the Arapaho fight. Under Jim's fatherly eye he'd become a seasoned mountain man. With more than usual care they picked their outfit.

"In Blackfoot country," Jim said, "we can't risk hunting meat or building cook fires. We'll have to pack plenty of pemmican."

First they killed several buffalo, cut the best meat into inch-thick strips and dried them on racks for five days. When the meat was hard they pounded it into powder with a mortar, emptied this into *parafleches,* or leather bags. Then they poured in melted fat, mixed in dry wild berries for flavor, and sewed the bags shut. Men could live for months on this high-energy food without growing sick of the taste.

After the first thaw they set out for what is now Montana. Spring runoff had turned the rivers into raging floods, and crossings were difficult. Slowly they worked north. Never had Jim seen so many beaver. Their packs grew heavy and they cached furs. They discovered no Indian sign but never relaxed their vigilance. They visited their traps in early morning or at dusk. During the day they hid in well-concealed bivouacs.

Late in June Jim decided they had stretched their luck far enough. So far they had traveled only after dark, but now their pemmican was gone. They had to hunt more meat. The next afternoon they were crossing a wooded river bottom when dozens of Indians suddenly swarmed out of the timber and surrounded them. Jim's heart sank. Somehow he'd blundered into a Blackfoot war party!

But he said to Dan, "Steady, son. Maybe we can still scrape through."

Walking boldly up to the leader, he made the sign of peace. The Blackfoot glowered at him and jerked his head. Disarmed and helpless, Jim and Dan followed him to a camp on the river bank. The head chief stepped from his tepee and stared at them. Their fate hung on the whim of this scowling ferocious savage.

The chief grunted a few words. Jim pretended he didn't understand. He didn't want them to guess that he could speak many phrases in the Blackfoot tongue. In sign language the chief demanded what two whites were doing in his domain. After Jim answered his questions, the chief brought out some buffalo meat and motioned them to eat.

"I can't swallow a mouthful," Dan muttered. "My stomach's doin' flipflops."

"Mine too," Jim admitted. "But he'll be insulted if we don't."

They forced down the meat and smoked their pipes. All the while more braves gathered around the tepee. Listening to their talk, Jim realized he must act soon. The Indians had been curious about their prisoners at first, where they came from and why, but now they were discussing how to kill them. "Don't let on we know what they're up to," he warned Dan. "They think we trust 'em because they fed us."

"It's almost dark," Dan said. "Let's run for it."

"Not yet. They're watching us too close. But keep your eye on me. Do what I do."

He waited until the chief got up to bring more tobacco. Several of the guards, absorbed in the debate, turned their backs. It was now or never, their only chance. Giving Dan the sign, he jumped to his feet and raced for the river. Stride for stride Dan ran beside him. An angry shout went up and the camp burst into an uproar. Guns boomed and bowstrings twanged. Straight between the tepees they sprinted to the bank and jumped in.

When Jim floated to the surface, it was too dark to see Dan. The yells of the enraged Blackfeet were deafening. With his face barely out of water he let the current carry him downstream. Silently he drifted to the far bank and groped along until he found an overhang screened by reeds. Neck deep in icy water, he ducked into this airpocket and clung to a root.

95

Carrying torches, the Indians hunted up and down the river. They kept up the search most of the night. Jim's body grew numb. Where was Dan? Had he drowned, or had they caught him? At last the Blackfeet gave up and withdrew to their camp. After daybreak they loaded their lodges on ponies and rode away. When Jim finally crept out on shore he had spent eight hours in the river.

For three days he hunted for his partner. There was a faint chance that Dan had escaped and gone on without him. Sick with remorse and grief, Jim headed south. The Blackfeet had taken his horses and all his outfit. He had only the clothes on his back. When he staggered into rendezvous at Bear Lake ten days later he looked like a walking skeleton.

A search party went out at once. They recovered most of the furs but found no trace of Dan. Dan Glover had disappeared. The others tried to comfort him, but Jim shook his head. Too many of his friends had died by violence in the mountains. He had trapped his last beaver.

Jed Smith and Bill Sublette urged him to reconsider. "We need another partner," Jed said. "You won't have to trap. You can handle the supply end of the business."

But Jim held firm. He was thirty-five years old.

For nine long years he had not seen any member of his family. "I thank you, boys," he said. "But I'm getting no younger. Now I've earned a stake maybe I'll settle down a while."

"Settle down?" Bill hooted. "Not you, Jim. Your stick don't float that way."

With genuine emotion he shook hands and said good-by to his comrades, most of whom he probably would never see again. His last job was to guide the company fur caravan back to the settlements. Climbing to his saddle, he looked up at the snow-capped peaks. It seemed impossible that he was leaving these mountains. Someday perhaps he would return. But the wild free life he had known as a trapper was gone forever.

St. Louis had grown so during his absence that he hardly recognized it when he led his pack train into the city that October. For the first few days he felt strange walking the crowded streets without a concern for Indians or blizzards or stampeding buffalo. He slept in a bed and ate at a table, enjoying the comforts of civilization. Newspaper reporters sought him out for interviews, and he dined with General Ashley and other leaders of the state.

After settling his affairs and sending money to Dan Glover's family, he found that he'd earned nearly six thousand dollars on his final hunt. Not a fortune. But ample for his modest wants. Laden with presents, he hurried east across Illinois and Indiana. Here too he was astounded by all the changes. Villages and farms stretched the length of the Ohio Valley.

With a thumping heart he rode up to the familiar old farmhouse in Stark County. Would anybody remember him after so many years? A small boy stared at him across the yard. "My name's Jim Clyman," the boy said. "What's yours?"

A lump came to Jim's throat. "I'm Jim too. Reckon I'm your Uncle Jim."

The others rushed out to welcome him with cries of joy. The wanderer, their famous relative, had returned from the land of beyond. For Jim it was a wonderfully happy homecoming. All his brothers and sisters were married, farming in the vicinity and raising families. He visited back and forth, always in demand by his nephews and nieces, who sat spellbound by the hour while he told them stories of his adventures in the Rockies.

"Now you're home to stay," John told him, "we'll have to find you a wife."

"No you don't. I might just wander off again."

The following spring he did. Returning to Illinois,

he bought some land in the region he had surveyed back in 1821, and brought John and Lancaster west to farm it. Then he built a store in the town of Danville and took in a partner. But as Jim himself admitted, he was no businessman at heart. He spent too much time away from the store roaming about the countryside. While he was gone the partner ran up large debts and Jim had to sell some of his farms.

Then in June 1832 the Black Hawk War broke out. Black Hawk was a respected chief whom the Government had ordered to move, with all his people, the Sac and Fox tribes, out of Illinois across the Mississippi River. The younger braves rebelled. Quarrels led to bloodshed and finally to raids by both Indians and white men. Black Hawk decided to fight to get back his land.

A call went out for the militia to mobilize. Isolated settlers packed up their wagons and fled to safety. It seemed like the War of 1812 all over again. Jim got down his rifle and oiled it. "You old war horse," Lan said. "If there's a fight you can't stay out."

Jim didn't think this would be much of a fight. The Sacs and Foxes were not like the fierce western tribes —the Rees, Blackfeet and Sioux. But few men in Illinois had his knowledge of Indian warfare. To help put down the uprising was his duty. "Truth is," he said, "I'm tired of storekeeping. Man needs a little excitement now and then."

With his friend James Reed he enlisted in a volunteer company. They marched and drilled and waited for orders to attack. The men grew restless and bored. One evening Reed led a tall young gawky recruit up to Jim's tent. "I've been telling everybody what a wrestler you are, Jim," Reed said. "This young fellow thinks he can beat you two falls out of three."

Catch-as-catch-can wrestling was a popular sport along the frontier. Jim smiled and stepped forward. Although he was forty years old now, he was stronger and more wiry than most men half his age. The stranger looked to be all awkward arms and legs. "I'm game," Jim said. "Start whenever you're ready."

A crowd gathered to watch the fun. Confidently Jim circled around, maneuvering for a hold. Suddenly a hand shot out and seized his wrist in a grip of steel. Jim went flying through the air and landed on his back with a thud that made him dizzy. In thirty seconds he'd lost the first fall.

With new respect he faced his opponent for the second fall. Cautiously he moved about, feinting and dodging, trying to keep beyond reach of those powerful hands until he figured out the other's style. Then he darted in and got an arm lock. But Jim was no match for the young man's strength. The stranger broke the lock easily, threw and pinned him to the ground. The whole bout had lasted less than five minutes.

As they got to their feet the young man thrust out his hand. "It was a put-up job, Mr. Clyman. I'm the champion wrestler in my part of the state."

Jim gave him a rueful grin. "You won fair and square. But where did a sprout like you get those muscles?"

"Splitting fence rails mostly."

"What's your name, son?"

"Abe," the stranger said. "Abe Lincoln."

9. FOUNDER OF A CITY

Y EARS later Abraham Lincoln said that the only fighting he did in the Black Hawk War was with mosquitoes. But during the few weeks they served together young Abe and Jim became friends. Abe had a keen mind, an endless curiosity. The year before, he had made a trip down the Mississippi to New Orleans. He told Jim, "I never realized before how big this country of ours is. Bigger than a man can dream."

In turn Jim told him about the vastness of the western plains and mountains, the geography of the Rockies and Great Basin. "It's no dream," he said, "although my trapper friends used to laugh at me. Some day all that country will be filled up. Maybe

102

you and I won't live to see it, but the time's bound to come."

"I think you're right, Jim," Abe Lincoln said. His face clouded. On his journey he had been shocked by the conditions of slavery he had witnessed in the South. "And when it does come, I pray that those settlers will be free Americans, not black slaves."

At last the company was ordered into action. They marched to the Whitewater River and searched the area, but the Indians fled. Not one soldier fired a shot. Shortly afterward Jim was commissioned a lieutenant and transferred to the Rangers under Colonel Henry Dodge. In the meantime Black Hawk, a skillful tactician, had swooped down on an infantry battalion, inflicted heavy casualties and melted away again. Jim led out a patrol to re-establish contact.

Black Hawk had about four hundred in his band, including women and children, while the combined American forces numbered several thousand. This chief was too wily to let himself be trapped east of the Mississippi, Jim reasoned. More likely, he would retreat and cross to the western side of the river. Scouting on that theory, the Rangers soon found his trail.

Three regiments closed in to attack. But once

again Black Hawk fought free and continued his withdrawal. For ten days the Americans tried to catch him, chasing through swamps and deep brushy canyons. The Indians weakened fast. Their trail was marked by the dead who fell in exhaustion. For a third time they almost escaped but on August 2 the troops cornered them at the mouth of Bad Axe River.

Concealed by early morning mist, Black Hawk fought bravely in the timbered bottoms, but he was hopelessly outnumbered. Rather than see all his people destroyed, he surrendered. Afterward Jim seldom talked about his part in the campaign. He'd done his job. But the behavior of some of the troops sickened him. They mutilated the bodies of the Indians and even yanked out their teeth to keep as souvenirs.

"No wonder Indians hate us," he said. "We sign a treaty with them and break it. Then butcher them like animals."

As a result of Black Hawk's treatment, unrest spread to other tribes. Jim's battalion marched north into the territory of Wisconsin and spent the next few months rounding up the scattered Winnebagos for removal to reservations. The Winnebagos were bitter at being uprooted from their ancestral home, but they submitted without a fight. Later this bitterness exploded into an incident that almost cost Jim his life.

For two years, until the neighboring tribes were pacified, he served in the Rangers and then resigned. When he returned to Danville his business affairs were in such a tangle that he sold his store. At that time Wisconsin was pretty much a wilderness, with only a few small settlements. Fondly he recalled its forests and sparkling lakes, still unspoiled by the hand of man. Restless for the frontier, he left Illinois with a friend to make a fresh start.

They built a sawmill and Jim established claim to some government land near the shores of Lake Michigan. But other land-hungry settlers soon followed him. Before long his claim became the site of a village called Milwaukee. Squatters camped on his property, laid out streets and surveyed lots. The country was getting too crowded again. In disgust he moved on north into the wilderness to search for more land.

One afternoon in the fall of 1835 he and a companion, Ellsworth Burnett, came to a wigwam on the bank of the Rock River. The only occupant, a Winnebago squaw, seemed harmless. Many Winnebagos wandered about the woods to fish and hunt. Jim and Burnett bargained with her and bought a birchbark canoe for fifty cents. Loading in their gear, they paddled downriver a mile or so to an abandoned trapper's shack, where they stepped ashore. "There's a nip in the air," Jim said. "Let's sleep inside tonight."

"Might as well," Burnett agreed. "I'll clean out the place while you rustle some firewood."

Meanwhile the squaw's husband, Here-I-Stand, and her son, Little Chief, returned to the wigwam. When they learned that two white men had passed by they flew into a rage. Not long before, the squaw's brother had been shot and killed by a sentry at Fort Winnebago. Here-I-Stand had sworn revenge on all whites. This was his chance.

Jim had leaned his shotgun against the cabin and was off some distance when the two Indians approached on foot, smiling and apparently friendly. Burnett was inside lighting a fire. They both walked in while Jim went on collecting wood. Most of the Winnebagos had settled down as peaceful citizens, and he had no reason to distrust this pair.

A sudden rifle blast shattered the evening quiet. Burnett screamed in agony. Jim whirled around. The old buck stepped to the door and motioned him to hurry. In the Winnebago tongue he called that Burnett had shot himself accidentally and needed help. Jim ran forward. But as he neared the cabin

Here-I-Stand reached inside and whipped a rifle to his shoulder.

Jim had never been closer to death than in that instant. Of all the Indians he had fought—to be duped by such a trick! He turned and ran for the trees, dodging from side to side in a zigzag. The Indian took aim and fired. The heavy ball smashed Jim's left arm below the elbow and knocked him down. Stunned by the pain, he staggered to his feet and stumbled on. The clearing seemed miles across. He could hear Here-I-Stand yelling and frantically reloading his rifle.

Then Little Chief jumped through the doorway. He had surprised Burnett and killed him with the first shot, but now his rifle was empty. Grabbing up Jim's loaded shotgun, he fired a long-range blast of buckshot into Jim's thigh. Jim managed to limp into the shelter of the timber, though blood was pouring down his wounded leg. The two Indians came after him at a run.

He had a fair lead, perhaps fifty yards, and the light was fading fast. Could he keep ahead of them until dark? He ran until the loss of blood made him weak and giddy. Not far behind his pursuers called out to each other as they hunted for his tracks. Just ahead was a large fallen tree. Jim crawled under the trunk and burrowed down among the dead branches.

The two Winnebagos trotted up to his hiding place. Little Chief jumped on the log, a few feet above Jim's head, and peered about the trees. "The other white man is dead," Jim heard him say.

"We shall find and kill this one also," Here-I-Stand said. "He is wounded. We have seen his blood. He cannot go far."

Jim lay rigid. How many of his friends had fallen to Indians? Reed Gibson, Pierre LaBarge, Dan Glover, a long sad list of others. And now El Burnett. Was his turn next? "We must hurry," Little Chief said, "before night comes."

Still searching, they moved off and vanished in the gloom, silent on moccasined feet. Not until darkness closed over the forest did he creep out. Shivering in the chill November night, he said a prayer of thanks for his deliverance. But he was far from safe yet. The nearest settlement where he could get help, Milwaukee, lay fifty miles across an unbroken wilderness.

At the river bank he washed his arm wound and wrapped his handkerchief around it. Supporting his left arm in his right hand, he headed south at a slow hobbling gait. By daylight he must be far from the cabin. The Winnebagos still might try to follow him. He waded up creeks and climbed over rocks to confuse his trail. Again and again he had to stop and rest.

About midnight a rainstorm set in. The downpour would wipe out his footprints, but it drenched his numb body to the skin. He floundered on through mud and rising streams. Only his iron constitution, and a burning desire to avenge Burnett's murder, kept him going. At daybreak he wormed into a thicket and dozed for an hour or so. No sign of pursuit. He tottered on.

Traveling all that day, he grew steadily weaker. His arm throbbed with every step. Feverish and dizzy, he began to talk aloud to himself. "Mustn't lie down again. If I do I'll never get up. Got to stay on my feet."

Mile after mile he fought his way forward through the dripping forest. That second night he thought he would surely collapse and die. By noon of the third day he was near the end of his strength. Then he heard the ringing blows of an ax. A few minutes later he staggered into a clearing. His awful journey was over. He had reached the outskirts of Milwaukee, the farm of his friend John Bowen.

With a shout Bowen ran across the field. He took

one shocked look and helped Jim to his cabin, hustled him into bed. There was no doctor handy. Bowen treated Jim's wounds himself. For several weeks Jim recuperated. It was to be a year before he regained full use of his shattered arm, and for a long time he walked with a limp. Few other men could have survived such an ordeal.

Until his escape from the Winnebagos he had been regarded by the villagers as a gruff silent woodsman who preferred to be left alone. But now his fame spread. His former commander, Henry Dodge, the new governor of Wisconsin, appointed him a colonel in the territorial militia. Fifty people, in sympathy with his plight, signed a paper requesting the U. S. Congress to award him a square mile of bounty land.

One day a delegation called on him. Jim's throat tightened as he read the words of the petition. . . . *singular traits of character . . . daring spirit . . . one of the most honorable and worthy citizens of Milwaukee.* This is what his neighbors thought of him.

He was deeply touched. But he declined their offer with thanks. He needed no favors from the Government. "I'm mighty grateful," he told the group. "But I can still take care of myself."

A search party went to Rock River. The men buried Burnett and brought back Jim's shotgun—the same gun that had wounded him—which they'd found beside the cabin. As soon as he was able to travel again he rode to Fort Winnebago in the hope of finding some trace of Burnett's murderers. But they had disappeared somewhere in the north woods.

"Do you know what these Indians call you now?" Bowen asked him. *"Jibbinenosey.* That's Shawnee for 'The Devil.' They're scared to death of you."

"My reputation can't be that bad," Jim said. But one morning when he entered a store where several Indians were lounging they edged away uneasily and slunk out the door. Any man who had lived through so many Indian fights, they knew, must be dangerous indeed.

He only laughed when a newspaper reporter wrote about him:

> He is a perfect gentleman, courteous and dignified to all, but a dangerous foe when aroused. He possesses the keenest sight of any man I know. He seldom shows any emotion, except when an Indian is in sight, when an expression appears upon his face not difficult to interpret, one that bodes no good to the Indian. He is a splendid woodsman; no better ever lived, and he has wonderful powers of endurance.

Such praise embarrassed him. He had no wish to harm peaceful Indians. In fact, abuse of them made him angry, because in the end it always led to more violence and bloodshed.

Some eighteen months went by before Here-I-Stand and Little Chief were captured and brought to trial for their crime. A jury found them guilty. Before the judge pronounced sentence, however, a number of Winnebagos signed a petition begging the governor to pardon them. Henry Dodge sent for Jim. "There's a lot of strong feeling about this on both sides," he explained. "What do you think?"

As a Ranger, Jim had been one of those who forced the tribe to give up their lands. He could see the Indian side of any question, whether they were Snakes or Winnebagos. In some ways he even felt and thought like an Indian. "For a long time," he told the governor, "I could hardly wait to get my hands on that pair. But hanging them won't bring Burnett back."

"Your opinion carries weight in this territory, Jim. I'll go along with whatever you recommend."

Jim had often pondered the problem of Indian rights versus the white man's rights. Some day, he believed, the two races must learn to get along together. "If you do hang them," he said, "it'll stir up a lot more bad feeling. I'm not one to hold a

112

grudge forever. I say let bygones be bygones. Turn 'em loose."

Governor Dodge shook his hand. "That's a true Christian spirit. I'm glad you see it that way."

So he signed a pardon of expediency and ordered Here-I-Stand and Little Chief released. Jim never saw them again, for they took care to avoid him. Many settlers criticized this action. But time proved him right. The Winnebagos, as a tribe, caused no more trouble in Wisconsin.

10. TRAIL GUIDE

DURING these years Jim became a land scout. Hundreds of settlers were pouring into Wisconsin and he scouted ahead into the wilderness to find unclaimed land, then helped them locate on it and file their papers. Often he was called upon to settle boundary line disputes between settlers and unscrupulous speculators. Known as "Colonel Clyman," he won a name for his fair dealings. He liked this work, which kept him on the move, and prospered at it. But he never took land and settled down himself.

John Bowen kept after him. "You've roamed more country than any dozen men, Jim. Can't you find a place to your liking?"

Jim had no ready answer. He had seen many beautiful places, ideal sites for a home or farm, from the Blue Ridge of Virginia to the Rockies. But he had never found the spot that suited him perfectly. "Guess I just like to keep looking," he said.

"You marry some good woman," Bowen told him. "She'll settle you down in a hurry."

Jim laughed. "Who'd want to marry a rolling stone like me?" His friends were always trying to marry him off. They considered him a good catch. But the truth was he had never fallen in love.

For a while he returned to Illinois, where he took on the job of placing milestones along a new road that led to the village of Chicago. He had grand-nieces and grand-nephews now. His hair was flecked with gray, and he walked with a slight stoop from years of carrying heavy packs, but he covered the ground with a long, tireless stride. He was still as tough as a hickory knot.

Not long after his fifty-first birthday he developed a bad cough that hung on through February and March. The weather continued wet and miserable. Troubled by pains in his chest, he made plans to travel south to a warmer climate. He took a horse, his saddle roll and rifle and his spaniel dog Lucky. "Same old Jim," his brother said. "You always travel light."

"Indian style. That's good enough for me."

"How long will you be gone this time?"

"Maybe a few months. Till I get rid of this cough."

Being on the go again was like a tonic. Quickly he recovered. He rode south into Arkansas, camping and hunting and fishing far from any settlements, accompanied by only his dog. For nearly a year he wandered about, then turned north toward Missouri. In the spring of 1844 he jogged into the bustling town of Independence.

Since his trapping days the frontier had moved several hundred miles west. Independence was now the jumping-off place for caravans bound to Oregon, California and New Mexico. Steamboats had replaced the old keelboats. Some fifteen hundred emigrants, eager to settle new land in the Far West, were camped outside town waiting for the first grass to spring up so they could begin their two-thousand-mile journey. They must have grass, grass to feed the oxen and mules and horses that would pull their big canvas-topped wagons—the prairie schooners.

The sight brought a thrill to Jim. All these Americans on the march! And not just men but whole families, from every corner of the United States, moving west with their household furniture and plows and tools and books and livestock—to start a new life in a land none of them had seen.

Anvils clanged and forges glowed as blacksmiths

reshod the animals and hammered tire irons on the wagon wheels. Women repacked their precious belongings and learned how to cook over open wind-blown fires. Children darted about playing "Indian," while their parents worried about the real Indians they soon would encounter. Men jammed the streets and stores of Independence, buying last-minute supplies, discussing routes and hardships of the trail ahead.

What impressed Jim was the cheerful spirit of these people. To them all, Oregon or California was the Promised Land. Nothing could turn them back. They argued and disagreed, but settled their disputes in democratic meetings where each had his say. They organized into companies and elected the most able as their leaders. And each day they studied the soil for the first green fuzz of grass, the signal to set out on the biggest adventure of their lives.

Reluctant to start back for Illinois, Jim spent several days about the town. One evening he bumped into a friend. A bearded man in buckskins peered into his face. "Jim!" he roared. "Jim Clyman, you old trap robber! Ain't clapped eyes on you since Hector was a pup."

"Black!" Jim exclaimed. "Black Harris! What brings you here?"

117

"I'm pilot for this wagon train." The man who had taught him how to catch a beaver pumped Jim's hand. "Come on. We got a heap o' lyin' to catch up on."

Black dragged him off to his camp and they sat up through the night yarning about old times. The fur trade, Black mourned, was finished. Styles had changed, nobody wore beaver hats any more, the streams were trapped out. Friend after friend had been killed by Indians: Jed Smith by Comanches on the Santa Fe Trail, Hugh Glass and Cutnose by the Rees. Most of those "enterprising young men" who answered General Ashley's newspaper ad had passed on to their Last Rendezvous. Only a hardy handful, like Bill Sublette and Tom Fitzpatrick and Black himself, still roved the mountains.

"We'll be pullin' out for Oregon any day now," he said. "Why don't you come along, Jim?"

"Me? All the way to Oregon?"

"The prettiest country a man ever saw," Black said. "I can use some help, too. Five hundred pilgrims in my train."

"But I've never been that far west."

Black snorted. "You could lead 'em there and back with blinders on. I'll get you a job."

Jim felt a tug of excitement. Why not? He wanted

118

to be a part of this great migration. On the far Pacific shore maybe he would find the land of his dreams, start a new life too. It was a challenge his restless blood could not resist.

Next day Black introduced him to the captain of his train, Colonel Nat Ford. "Meet Jim Clyman, Nat," Black said. "A lucky day for us when he happened along. Knows more 'bout Injuns than they know theirselves."

Responsible for so many green emigrants, Ford was delighted to have a veteran like Jim. On the spot he hired him as assistant guide. Jim bought a few horses and some extra gear, then got acquainted with the members of his mess. The train was divided into groups of twenty, who would share their food and the chores of cooking. These twenty would be his companions for the next few months.

Rain had fallen steadily for weeks. The roads were boggy mires. Colonel Ford wanted to wait until the weather cleared. But Jim and Black advised against delay. "The first party to leave will get the best of everything," Jim said. "Grass, firewood, game. Late starters'll have slim pickings."

Black nodded. "Five hundred folks and fifteen hundred head o' stock. They'll cut a swath like an army."

So the date was set. Excitement mounted as the news spread through camp. The first grass was up! On the gray stormy morning of May 14 the wagons began to form in line. Whips popped, teamsters hawed at their oxen, and cattle milled about in the mud. But Jim and Black had bossed many a caravan before. Shouting commands, they rapidly brought order out of confusion. Prairie schooners creaked into their assigned positions.

"Wagons, ho!" The cry passed along the column. Wheels churned and trace chains jingled. Under leaden skies the first train of 1844 rolled westward.

The downpour kept up as they crept through the wooded hills into open prairie. They sloshed along through knee-deep water. Small creeks grew into torrents and every crossing was a struggle. One stream rose seven feet overnight. Jim rode ahead searching for passable fords, with Lucky trotting at his heels.

At each river men cut a roadway down the slippery banks. Since the wagons had no brakes, they chained the wheels and tied on logs behind to serve as a drag. Sometimes they double- and triple-teamed to pull wagons through the swirling yellow current and sucking mud. Some banks were so high they un-hitched and lowered the wagons by rope. At the

Kansas River they cut down trees, lashed the logs together into rafts and ferried across. Not long afterward the river overflowed and covered the countryside with a sheet of water ten miles wide.

One day the skies would clear. But the next, thunder and lightning would usher in a new storm. People sniffled with colds and grumbled about their sodden clothes and blankets. Even Black Harris complained. "Man dassn't lie down he'll git the rheumatiz. Dassn't stand up or he'll git hit by lightnin'."

Slowly they advanced into Kaw territory, where Jim crossed the trail he had blazed seventeen years before. Leaving the swampy low country, he led the train along a chain of high ridges. Travel was harder here but they had some protection against raiding Pawnees. Both Kaws and Pawnees were supposedly friendly, but the white man's horses were a powerful temptation. Every night he had the emigrants corral their stock and post guards.

When some complained about these precautions, Jim explained to the wagonmaster: "These tribes are government wards. But they don't get enough food and they hate to farm. So they steal horses to trade or hunt with."

For several days large numbers of Kaws trailed

121

along behind. At night they camped outside the wagon enclosure, begging sugar and tobacco. Despite Jim's warning, the guards grew lax. To them these Indians seemed like good-natured children. Then one morning they awoke to find the Kaws gone, along with three valuable horses.

Jim at once set out to follow. For two days he hunted through draws and brushy creek bottoms but lost the trail in the rain. He caught up with the slow-moving caravan, rested a day and made another unsuccessful search. A week had passed since the theft and the emigrants thought he would give up now. He told them, "Maybe I'm stubborn. But if the Kaws get away with it they'll rob every train that comes through this year. And next time it won't be three horses. They'll stampede a whole herd."

The following morning a halfbreed named Jo reported that he knew where the thieves were hiding. His story had the ring of truth. So Jim rode off on a third attempt. All that day Jo led him through a driving rain, across creeks so deep they had to swim. At dusk, as the rain turned into hail, they approached a lonely sod-roofed dugout where a few ponies stood tethered.

As the searchers ducked inside they saw about twenty drunken Kaws squatted on the floor chanting. Two Indians brandishing knives leaped toward Jo. Jim drew his pistol and fired into the roof. In that small airless room it sounded like a thunderclap. The uproar stopped abruptly. The knife wielders froze. Jim demanded his horses.

The Kaws denied any knowledge of them. Jim listened grimly. How many times had he heard that same tale? "They're lying," he said to Jo. "Tell them this: If the horses aren't returned by the time we reach the Blue River I'm coming back with fifty men. And I won't shoot through the roof."

It was a bluff. But the Kaws knew, and feared, a mountain man when they saw one. And this one, with his fierce eyes, surely must be a *jibbinenosey*, a devil.

Two days later a Kaw boy herded the three missing animals up to the wagons. They must have strayed away, he said. It was the Indian way of saving face. Jim smiled and gave him some candy. The train had lost its last horse to this tribe.

Finally the sun appeared. The trail dried out and the wagons rolled along at a faster clip, averaging as much as fourteen miles some days. At the Blue they stopped to rest the stock, mend harness and wash clothes. The children gathered wild currants and chokecherries and Jim shot a deer for his mess.

Spirits rose. After two months of almost steady rain the worst seemed over.

But so much time had been lost they had to press on at top speed. Snow came early in the western mountains, blocking the high passes. At Jim's urging the train got under way early and traveled late each day as they hurried up the valley of the Platte River. Twenty miles. Twenty-five. One day they made a record thirty miles.

But the trail was not always smooth. They had to detour around bluffs, fill in gullies, bridge washes, watch for quicksand fords. Once they were delayed for hours by an immense buffalo herd crossing their line of march. Fuel was scarce. Jim taught them to rig "possum bellies," sheets of canvas slung under the wagon beds, in which they carried whatever scraps of wood they could find. They cooked over dry grass, sagebrush and buffalo chips.

Whenever the children were sent out to gather berries or fuel Jim went along with his rifle, to guard them against grizzlies or surprise Indian attacks. He was a favorite with the youngsters, this quiet soft-spoken man who had no children of his own. He taught them trail craft. At night around the campfire, when the fiddles and mouth harps had been laid aside, and prairie wolves howled outside the corral, he would spin them stories. Many a small boy shivered with envy and secretly longed to grow up just like Jim Clyman.

On August 1 the caravan reached the tiny military post of Fort Laramie in Wyoming, the westernmost outpost of the U.S. Government. To the emigrants this seemed very far from home, a speck in the wilderness. And they were not yet half way!

Prices of supplies were sky high, a dollar for a pint of flour, two dollars for a cup of sugar. Even sending mail was a luxury. Eastbound travelers sometimes charged a dollar per letter to carry mail back to the settlements, with no assurance of delivery. Jim sent off a report on trail conditions, which he had promised to write for the Milwaukee newspapers.

"From here on," he told Nat Ford, "hold the wagons as close together as possible. We'll be passing through hostile territory. Tribes raid back and forth. Crows, Sioux, Arapahos, Utes."

Colonel Ford tried his best but it was impossible to keep a hundred wagons and all their livestock bunched. Stragglers fell behind and the faster outfits pushed ahead, until the train was spread out for miles. Five days west of Laramie Jim rode up on a ridge and signaled a halt. A large party of Indians was galloping across the plains.

Jim Clyman

Black Harris stared through his glass and handed it to Jim. "Sioux!" he said. "And they got their dander up, or this hoss can't read sign."

"Sioux all right," Jim agreed. "Headed straight for us."

11. OREGON

THE Indians reined to a stop several hundred yards away. Nervous emigrants fingered their rifles. If the Sioux decided to attack, Jim knew they could easily pick off stray wagons and perhaps overrun the whole train. But he had once fought at their side, as an ally in the Ree campaign. Leaving Black and Ford to calm the settlers, he rode ahead alone.

Watching anxiously, they saw him approach the Sioux and dismount. A chief stepped forward. The two men, Indian and white, squatted on the ground and smoked a pipe. They talked. The parley lasted an hour. Then Jim remounted and rode back up the ridge. The Sioux wheeled away and raced off in the opposite direction. A sigh of relief went up along the wagon train.

"They don't want trouble," Jim explained, "any more than we do. But they were afraid we meant to settle here and kill off all the buffalo. This is their hunting ground."

"What'd you tell 'em, Jim?"

"That we're pushing straight through. We'll shoot a few buffalo for meat, but that's all. If we behave ourselves, they will."

The train got under way again. "That Clyman," one of his messmates said. "Cool as brass the way he braced those devils. I wouldn't have done that for all the money in the mint."

To Jim this had been only an incident. No troops were available to protect the emigrants on their long trek to Oregon. So the job fell to a few men like himself, who had learned through bitter experience how to handle Indians. He said to Black, "The Sioux will keep their word. But I pity the man who tries to take their land. They'll make these plains red with blood."

Every foot of the trail brought back memories. The caravan came to Independence Rock, which Tom Fitzpatrick had discovered years before. On it Tom and dozens of other old trapper friends had carved their names. A few days later the wagons crawled up over South Pass and Jim looked back over the long train, thinking of a raw winter day in 1824 when he had first stood here.

"Wagh!" Black said. "We like to froze to death that trip. No meat, no water but melted snow. Them was some doin's, Jim."

Jim nodded. He'd come back to the mountains after all. They looked the same. But now South Pass was a turnpike linking east to west, a thoroughfare across the continent.

Beyond the Green River they rolled into the trading post built by Jim Bridger and Louis Vasquez, their companion on the bullboat voyage around Salt Lake. The four old cronies had a lusty celebration and then got down to business. Many of the emigrants' oxen were footsore and lame from a thousand miles of rocky trail. Bridger offered to trade one sound ox, from his herd, for two lame animals.

"How do you make a profit that way?" Jim asked.

Bridger winked and led him to a big corral, which he had converted into a shallow muddy pond. He turned the lame oxen into his "puddle," Bridger explained, and within a few weeks the mud cured their hoofs. Then he traded them back to the next caravan over the trail. "Two for one," he laughed. "Beats beaver trappin', Jim. I sit here and let the money come to me."

It was now September. Water buckets froze every night and frost whitened the grass. Then a teamster named Barnett came down with an unknown fever. For several days he grew weaker. Colonel Ford had to make a hard decision. Barnett was too sick to survive much more jolting in a wagon. But to halt the train for several days might endanger the life of every emigrant.

"No need for that." Jim spoke up. "You and Black take the train on, Nat. I'll stay behind with Barnett."

So Jim and six other men camped beside the trail, with only one wagon and their horses, while the rest of the caravan rolled on. At first Barnett rallied. Then he was seized by spasms and became delirious, crying out for his friends. Jim dosed him with calomel and wrapped him in blankets. For three days and nights he seldom left the wagon. On the fourth night Barnett regained consciousness, smiled up at him and died.

Jim had done his best, for a man he scarcely knew, but Barnett's suffering had affected him deeply. With a heavy heart he wrote in his diary: *He departed this life without a struggle and all his troubles are in silent death*. They dug a deep grave, covered it with rocks to keep coyotes and wolves from the body.

By riding hard, Jim's group overtook the train

near Fort Hall. They lingered only a few hours at this outpost of the Hudson's Bay Company, the giant British fur combine whose trappers once had been his rivals. From here on they would be traveling through territory claimed by both the United States and England. The train pressed on across Idaho along the Snake River through a barren land of sage and lava rock. At the next trail junction thirteen wagons turned off to the southwest, bound for California. Jim had an urge to join them; he'd heard much of California from Jed Smith. But he was committed to the Oregon division. With many a hearty handclasp and tearful farewell the two parties separated.

Then Jim and Black and Nat Ford put their heads together. The rains back in Kansas had held the train a month behind schedule and food supplies were dangerously low. Game was scarce in the country ahead. "We can't travel any faster," Ford said. "Most of our oxen and mules are worn down."

"Send somebody ahead to Oregon on horseback," Jim told him. "To bring back food in case the wagons get caught in the snow."

"Passel of Injuns 'tween here and there," Black pointed out. "Mighty risky for a lone express."

131

Jim grinned. "I'm elected. And I'll pick three other bachelors. We'll get through."

Colonel Ford agreed. Some of the emigrants had relatives in Oregon already, men who had crossed the plains the year before. They would help if necessary. So next morning Jim's small band, mounted on fast horses, left the slow-moving wagons behind.

The nights were cold but the days were torments of heat and dust and burning sun. The whole country was parched. The occasional Indians they met, Nez Percés and Bannocks, were friendly, but near the Blue Mountains they ran into trouble with another tribe—the Cayuses. One night Jim was awakened by Lucky's frantic barking. He stepped out to investigate and saw a Cayuse, astride his favorite mare, driving off two mules.

Jim had left his rifle in camp but he gave a yell. The Indian jumped off and vanished in the night. The following day a band of Cayuses cut in ahead on the trail and galloped out of sight. Shortly black clouds of smoke billowed up and a wall of flame, fanned by a north wind, swept toward the four whites. The Cayuses had set the tinder-dry grass of the prairie afire.

It was a terrifying sight. Flames crackled and popped, leaping high in the air, spreading faster than a man could run. The horses bucked and plunged in terror as the smoke pall blotted out the sun. Plains tribes sometimes did this to stampede game or harass emigrants. Jim had known such fires to rage unchecked for weeks and burn over hundreds of square miles. But he'd never been caught in one before.

"We passed a creek back yonder!" John Minto panted. "We better make for that."

"Let's try a backfire." Often a second fire would blaze across the path of the first. When the two met, like giants in battle, they burned each other out. Jim knelt in the grass with his flint and steel, but before he could strike a spark the wind veered suddenly. It swung around to the south and blew the fire before it. With a prayer on his lips he watched the flames recede across the blackened prairie.

For two days they traveled through a smoldering desolation. The fire had spread to the mountains, destroying great stands of timber and driving all wild life before it. To see such waste saddened Jim. But they crossed the range without further trouble and rode into a Cayuse village in the valley below.

Minto gave a whoop. "You see what I see?" He pointed. "A potato patch!"

"Look out for these bucks," Jim warned. "They may be the ones who tried to burn us out."

But all four men were starved for potatoes and starch. They hadn't tasted anything but meat and fish in weeks. "It's my birthday today," Minto said. "I'm having 'taters for supper no matter what they cost."

He traded his shirt for six potatoes, freshly dug from the earth. The hungry Americans cut them up and gobbled the slices raw. Smacking his lips, Jim agreed that he'd never enjoyed a birthday banquet more. Then a squaw ran from her lodge with Minto's shirt. It was worn out, she wailed, and demanded the potatoes back.

Minto laughed and patted his stomach. "Sorry, ma'am. Too late."

A crowd of angry Cayuse braves gathered around. The chief strode into their midst, twirling a lasso, and flipped it at Minto. "Party's over, boys," Jim said. He leveled his rifle. "You were paid a fair price for your potatoes," he told the chief. "We're leaving now and don't try to stop us."

The chief stared into his eyes and lowered the rope. The others fell back to make a path. Jim led his men to their horses and rode on.

They were on the home stretch now, nearing the settlement of Oregon City, but one final barrier remained—the mighty Cascade Range. No wagons and few white men had ever crossed it. Emigrants preferred the Columbia River, in spite of its treacherous rapids. But Jim was in a hurry and he took the shortest route. Following an Indian trail, he climbed past Mt. Hood, through forests of fir and pine, fording icy snow-fed streams. This was the hardest part of the entire journey. They fought over the summit, through bogs and tangles of snags, down into the Willamette Valley.

The morning of October 13 they broke camp for the last time. Using a creek for a mirror, Jim shaved off his two-month growth of beard. He brushed the mud off his coat and donned a new shirt he had saved. The men laughed and joked as they spruced up, full of happy anticipation. A few more miles would see them back in civilization again. Ragged and tattered as they were, each wanted to look his best for the occasion.

That afternoon they filed over a ridge and came upon a clearing, the first farm they had passed since leaving Missouri. Thirty minutes later they circled a Chinook village and looked down upon the falls of the Willamette River and a straggling collection of some sixty log houses. A little girl stared at them shyly and two dogs bounded out to sniff these strange newcomers. Oregon City! The seat of government, capital of this remote American colony by the far Pacific.

Nobody cheered or tossed his hat in the air. It was a solemn moment. Jim led his weary men down the street and dismounted before the largest building. Over its roof waved the Stars and Stripes. One hundred and fifty-one days west of Independence he had reached the end of the Oregon Trail.

The first man to shake his hand was a friend with whom he had served as a Ranger in the Black Hawk War. Quickly Jim and the others organized relief riders, who hurried back to meet the oncoming train with food. Within a few weeks Black Harris herded the last of the wagons over the mountains into safety. They had beaten the winter snows.

In writing for the Milwaukee newspapers, Jim described the journey as "uneventful." So it was to him. The train had come through without the loss of a wagon. Of the five hundred emigrants only one had died—from disease. But within a few years the Oregon Trail would be lined with graves, mostly unmarked and soon forgotten. Hundreds of men, women and children were to die from cold and exhaustion and starvation and Indian attack. They were the unfortunate, who didn't have a Jim Clyman to lead them through to the Promised Land.

12. TROUBLE BREWING

SHORTLY after Jim's arrival the American agent for Indians in Oregon, Elijah White, called on him. In 1844 Oregon was not yet a territory of the United States. To the south lay the Mexican province of California. To the north lay British Canada. England and the United States were still arguing about where the northern boundary line should be established.

The English insisted that the boundary be the Columbia River. Americans claimed it should be much farther north, clear to the parallel line of $54°40'$. A few, ready to go to war with Britain again, had coined the slogan, "Fifty-Four Forty or Fight." Although American settlers had streamed into the country in the past two years, most of the trade and

137

commerce was controlled by the Hudson's Bay Company from nearby Fort Vancouver. This was the touchy situation White explained to Jim.

"Colonel Clyman," he said, "I hope to be appointed governor when Oregon is made a territory. But some of our government leaders back in Washington hardly know that Oregon exists. We've got to stir them to action."

"How?" Jim wanted to know.

"I'd like you to make a study of this country—its natural resources, crops, its future potential. Then write a report. I'll submit it to Congress in person."

"But why me, Mr. White? I just got here."

"Because," said the agent, "your experience and reputation are well known. Your opinions command respect. Working together I'm sure we can accomplish some good."

Jim was too modest to think that his views would influence Congress, but he undertook the job. In doing so he hoped to find some land on which he might settle some day. For the next few months he rode back and forth across the country, making friends with farmers and asking endless questions. As a former farmer himself, he studied the soil and weather conditions, inspected livestock herds and newly planted orchards. He made a survey of the timber, salmon fisheries, water power and the navigable rivers. Before long his notebooks were crammed with facts.

He interviewed men who had visited the country north of the Columbia, in what is now the state of Washington, and learned about Puget Sound. All insisted that this region, with its great natural harbor, should belong to the United States. Then he rented a skiff and rowed down the Willamette to the British stronghold of Fort Vancouver.

Dr. John McLoughlin, a Scotsman known throughout the northwest as the "Great White Eagle," had been post factor for years. He welcomed Jim heartily and for hours they talked about the old days in the fur trade. "Even here the fur is almost finished," McLoughlin admitted. "Soon Oregon will be covered with farms. You have traveled much, Colonel. What do you think of our problems?"

"I'll be frank, Doctor," Jim told him. "Every month more Americans are settling north of the Columbia, against your policy. They'll fight if anyone tries to stop them."

McLoughlin sighed. "Only Her Majesty's Government in London can decide that. I simply follow orders. But I hope our two countries can settle this boundary dispute without war."

"Every American in Oregon considers you his friend," Jim said. "You've helped all these emigrants. They arrive here starving, in rags, and you give them food and clothes and help. But they mean to keep their land."

"Thank you, sir." The Scotsman's eyes twinkled. "And I suppose that you too will stay and farm."

"No," Jim said slowly. Much as he had come to love Oregon, its vast forests and snow-capped peaks, he still felt the itch to move on. Maybe, beyond the next range, he would find the land he'd been seeking for nearly forty years. "I'm heading south for California in the spring."

He prepared his report with care. First he described the Oregon Trail, its hardships and dangers, and the vital need of keeping open this line of communication. Then he described conditions in Oregon —the local government, the Indian problem and relations with the British. In conclusion, he urged Congress to vote for the speedy establishment of Oregon as a federal territory. This, he wrote, would strengthen commercial ties with China and Russia and all the countries on the Pacific.

Elijah White praised him for the report. Planning to travel east as soon as the rainy season ended, he urged Jim to come along as guide. But Jim declined.

His mind was made up. He wanted to see California. So now the agent asked him to take on another job.

A mission Indian, son of the chief of the Walla Walla tribe, had been murdered by an American named Grove Cook while on a trading expedition at Sutter's Fort in northern California. The enraged Walla Wallas had demanded revenge. If Cook were not returned in irons for punishment, they threatened to rise up and massacre every settler in Oregon. "We're sitting on a powder keg," White said. "And as Americans we're in the wrong. Colonel, will you see if you can persuade the Californians to arrest this Cook and send him back for trial?"

Jim promised to do what he could, and began to prepare for the journey. As soon as word spread, a number of emigrants asked to join him so they could travel together for protection. They would take no wagons, only horses. The country to the south was rough and mountainous, a wilderness for hundreds of miles, inhabited by many small hostile tribes—the Umpquas, Klamaths, Modocs and others. A trapper who had just been over the trail warned the group what to do in Indian country.

"Never camp in timber. Never let any Indians come among you. Keep careful watch day and night.

141

Never scatter after game or make any other division. Keep your guns in the best firing condition."

Jim smiled to himself. He had been taking the same precautions ever since he was big enough to hold a gun. "Lucky," he told his spaniel, "we've seen a lot of Indians the last year. I guess a few more won't scare us off."

One morning a young man rode into camp where Jim was busy packing supplies. He was an expert coachmaker and carpenter, the young man said, and he too wanted to go to California.

"Carpenter, eh?" Jim said. Among his party were several farmers, a sailor, a French hatter, a blacksmith. But no carpenters.

"Yes, sir," the stranger said. "I understand skilled workmen are in great demand there. I expect to find a job. I'd be mighty grateful if you took me along, Colonel Clyman."

Jim nodded. He too once had been an enterprising young man, striking out for new country. He liked the look of this James W. Marshall.

Early in June they got under way—thirty-five men, a widow and her three children. The rains had ended but most of the lowlands still were flooded. The column built rafts and forded swollen rivers, fought through swamps and bogs. Slowly they climbed mountain ridge after ridge. The few Indians he encountered were the most primitive Jim had ever seen. They wore no clothes, lived on insects and grass, and fled like wild animals at his approach.

But farther south Indians appeared in larger numbers, following the emigrants and camping near their overnight bivouacs. One evening a small group of whites decided to drive them away with gunfire. A hothead named Frank Greer was the ringleader. Jim said sternly, "Listen to me, all of you. Those Indians haven't done us any harm. But you kill one, they'll come down on us in hundreds. We'll have to fight our way to California. Put your guns away!"

The grumbling subsided. Next day when they forded the Rogue River Jim posted riflemen on either bank, and the crossing was made without incident. But not long afterward Greer and a friend captured a squaw, tied her up and brought her into camp. Furious, Jim forced them to release her. Another time Greer fired into a mass of Indians and wounded one. The others fled into the brush.

On July 4 Jim made camp beside a river and announced they would rest there a day, in observance of the national holiday. He rode ahead to scout the next day's trail. During his absence several Indians appeared on the opposite bank and fired a few arrows at the camp. "Look at them filthy vermin," Greer muttered. "This is one time old Clyman can't stop me."

He made a bet with two of his cronies that, while they covered him with rifles, he would swim the river and kill an Indian. The other emigrants protested but Greer cowed them into silence. Armed with a knife he paddled across the stream and surprised a lone Indian in the bushes. They grappled briefly and Greer stabbed him in the chest. He was climbing back out of the water with the bloody scalp just as Jim returned.

Jim was so angry he could hardly speak. In his long career he had fought many Indians and killed a few, but never in sheer cruelty. It had always been a matter of life or death. "You must be proud!" he lashed out. "A fine way to celebrate our Independence Day!"

"I showed them red devils," Greer said sullenly.

Jim's eyes blazed. "You're not only a murderer, Greer. You're a stupid fool. I'm taking your weapons. And if you touch another Indian I'll have you flogged."

Greer caused no more trouble. He knew Jim would do exactly as he threatened. Later Jim told young Marshall, "I'm no Indian lover. But they're human creatures, the same as you and me. Why can't we live and let live?"

He doubled his guards and hurried on through Indian country, down out of the mountains into the plains of the Sacramento Valley. This, at last, was California. A month after leaving Oregon he led his party through the gates of Sutter's Fort.

Far beyond the Mexican settlements the legendary Swiss, John Augustus Sutter, had established a huge ranch domain which he ruled like a feudal lord. Eight hundred Indians worked in his fields and vineyards and tended his cattle herds. A kindly man, Sutter made Jim welcome and hired several of the emigrants. The others went their separate ways.

Glad to see the last of Greer, Jim explained the purpose of his visit. Could Sutter help him arrest the American, Cook, for murdering a Walla Walla chieftain's son? Sutter promised to use what influence he had with the Mexican authorities, but Jim himself must press the case in Monterey, the capital.

"It is bad, this senseless killing of Indians," Sutter said. "One day they will explode like so—*boom!* And no white man will be safe." Then his face brightened. "But let us speak of more pleasant things."

Proudly he showed Jim the adobe wall of dried mud bricks which enclosed his many buildings. New

Helvetia, he called it, in honor of his homeland, Switzerland. With glowing eyes he described his plans for the future. The dream nearest Sutter's heart was to build a sawmill up in the mountains on the American River, where timber was plentiful. He would saw the logs into planks and float them down the stream, enough lumber to build a whole city.

"Always before this seemed impossible," Sutter said. "But now, Colonel, you bring me your young friend Marshall. A carpenter and mechanic. He will build my sawmill. I am in your debt, sir."

Once Jim had built a sawmill himself, the first in Wisconsin. But now his stick floated in another direction. "He's a good lad, Mr. Sutter. Jim Marshall will do you proud."

Trailed by the faithful Lucky, he rode south around the end of San Francisco Bay, past Mission San José, and arrived at Monterey. For the first time he looked upon the Pacific Ocean, saw American ships at anchor in the harbor. And in the streets of the sleepy village, capital of California, he heard more English spoken than Spanish.

At the office of Thomas Larkin, the American counsul, Jim introduced himself and presented his official documents. Larkin assured him he would appeal to the governor and do everything possible to arrest Cook. But he warned Jim not to count on it. The Californios had far graver problems on their minds. Their province was seething with rumors of revolution, of coming war between the United States and Mexico. They had no interest in the problems of far-off Oregon.

"They have problems with Indians here too," Jim said. "And they'll have a lot more if they ignore this murder. Can't you make the governor see how serious it is?"

The consul shrugged. "I can make suggestions, nothing more. My hands are tied, Mr. Clyman. And so are yours. We are foreigners here, and not very popular at the moment."

Disappointed at his failure, Jim left Monterey next day. Grove Cook was never brought to justice. The killing of an Indian or two seemed unimportant to many whites. But not to the Walla Wallas and other tribes of Oregon and northern California. All too soon the hatred planted by men like Cook and Greer flamed into warfare. Settlers and missionaries were massacred by the score. Years were to pass before an American could travel in safety from the Columbia overland to San Francisco Bay.

13. THE TRAIL EAST

DURING the next few weeks Jim and Lucky became familiar figures on the streets of Yerba Buena, as San Francisco was then called. Events were rushing toward a climax. Each ship that sailed into the harbor brought news of fresh trouble between the United States and Mexico. The politicians of both countries were clamoring for war. All foreigners, especially Americans, grew more unpopular. A Yankee skipper was attacked by an angry mob and almost killed. Jim made a vigorous protest to the Mexican officials through Consul Larkin, but nothing came of it.

The government of California was weak. It had no money in the treasury and few troops. Various factions were always scheming to march on Monterey and seize power for themselves. Three European nations — England, France and Russia — were rumored to be eying this ripe plum for their empires. A number of Americans accused of plotting rebellion had been arrested and thrown into jail.

"This town is no place for us if the kite goes up," Jim said to Lucky. "Let's go back to the mountains."

Up to that time he'd seen little of California that he liked. He had no respect for a government that treated Indians like slaves. The one industry was cattle raising and the selling of hides and tallow. The only fruit in the country was grown by the mission padres. But when he crossed the bay and rode north into Napa Valley to visit a trapper friend, his outlook changed. This was unlike any land he had known, a gentle sunny place of oak groves and rolling hills. Strangely he felt at home.

"A man can't beat this soil for crops," his friend told him. "Grab yourself some land, Jim, and settle down like me."

True, the soil was rich. Napa Valley lay on the edge of wilderness. Game of all kinds roamed the nearby mountains. Everything about it appealed to Jim. But this was a foreign country, subject to Mexican rule. "I'll think it over," he said.

He did build a temporary cabin and planted a vegetable plot. Still undecided, he went on a fall hunt for deer, elk and bear. Grizzlies were so numerous they often raided the settlers' livestock. In one week he killed nine of these savage predators. He traveled north into the giant redwood forests and saw his first condors, huge vultures with a wingspread of ten feet. He experienced his first earthquake.

Back at his cabin during the rainy season, he wrote a long report and kept busy in his garden. Then one March day in 1846 a messenger arrived with grim news. A U.S. Army officer, Captain John C. Frémont, leader of an exploration party, had run into trouble with Mexican authorities near Monterey and raised the American flag in a gesture of defiance. General Castro had called for four hundred volunteers to drive out the "Yankee invaders." The province trembled on the brink of war.

But Frémont held his men in check and withdrew. Castro hailed the retreat as a bloodless victory. Jim discussed the situation with his friends and hurried off to Frémont's camp. Perhaps Frémont had acted rashly, but he was a fellow American far from home and he needed help.

Frémont's force numbered sixty mountain men, many of whom had learned their trade under Jim in the old fur-trapping days. Kit Carson, Frémont's guide, introduced him to the young officer. "This is Jim Clyman, Captain," Kit said. "He was fighting Injuns when most of us were still in the cradle. And he's a colonel in his own right."

Frémont listened with interest. Secretly he hoped to play a key role in the conquest of California. In Jim he recognized a born leader, one who could do much to help his cause.

"I came to offer my services," Jim said. "You say the word, Captain, and I'll recruit fifty crack riflemen for you inside a week."

"How can you do that, sir?" Frémont asked.

"Every American here, and many Mexicans, are sick of this government. They know a change is coming. They'd rather see the Stars and Stripes over California than any other flag."

"And how long do you think such a campaign would take?"

"From what I've seen," Jim said, "I'm sure that a hundred good men, yours and mine, can capture this province in three months."

Frémont took a long time with his answer. As a representative of the United States, he said, he had no right to provoke war. His purposes in California were peaceful. He was a guest of the Mexican government. To ask Jim to enlist an armed force would be a hostile act. "I'm sorry, Colonel Clyman," he said. "If war does come then I'll need your support. But as a military man you can see my position. Technically we're at peace with Mexico. I'm leaving for Oregon at once."

Jim didn't argue. But he thought that John C. Frémont had chosen the wrong course, one that would leave hundreds of American settlers without military protection. As a result of this interview he decided to leave California himself. He had no wish to take up land in a country where revolution or war might break out any day.

"Throw in with us, Jim," Kit Carson urged him. "You've been over that Oregon route. We can use a guide."

Jim shook his head. "Any traveling I do will be through new country. Before I get too old, Kit."

"Old?" Kit chuckled. "I bet you can outlast any man in camp."

But Jim had made up his mind. He rode to Sutter's Fort to buy supplies and mules. John Sutter was full of war talk. Work on Jim Marshall's sawmill had been postponed. Some of Sutter's friends, disgusted with affairs in California, were heading back east soon, over a new route through the Sierra Nevada Mountains. Would Jim like to join them?

"How about it, old-timer?" Jim said to Lucky, and scratched his dog's ears. "We've seen a heap o' country. Maybe it's time we hit for home."

Lucky barked and licked his hand. Jim promised Sutter he would escort his party through to the settlements. Twenty years ago he had explored part of the Great Basin. This offered a chance to see more of it. He dried some beef and repaired his pack saddles, then climbed to a camp in the Sierras where the other travelers had assembled. Not all were homeward bound. Their leader, a young lawyer named Lansford Hastings, was going only as far as Jim Bridger's fort.

"California has a great future," Hastings explained, "but we need more American settlers." Most of the emigrants moving west, he said, were bound for Oregon. Hastings planned to meet them along the Oregon Trail, persuade them to change their route and come to California instead. He had written a book, *The Emigrant's Guide,* which he gave to Jim to read.

Jim found Hastings' book long on fancy words, but short on facts. It made a trip across the plains sound like a Sunday picnic. "This trail you describe," he asked, "the one west of Salt Lake. How much do you know about it?"

153

"Captain Frémont came that way last year," Hastings assured him. "It's four hundred miles shorter than the regular trail."

Late in April the group set out—nineteen men, three women and three small boys. Snow lay so deep they had to trample out a path for the animals. Not even the Rockies had seemed as rugged as these peaks of the high Sierra. Icy winds blew and avalanches thundered down the slopes. At one camp two starving wolves chewed up the lariats that tied the horses. Jim advised Hastings to wait until more snow melted from the passes, but Hastings was in a hurry. He feared he might miss the westbound wagon trains if he delayed.

They struggled to the summit, fighting through eight-foot drifts, and down the eastern side. The wind grew so strong it blew one woman off her saddle. To get down over sheer precipices they had to unload the horses, lower their supplies by rope and reload at the bottom. At night they chopped out level patches in the frozen snow for their tents. They suffered frostbite and exhaustion. One man was struck by snow blindness from the terrible sun glare.

At last the band straggled down to Truckee Lake and the welcome sight of green grass. They had covered six miles in three days. During that time the horses and mules had gone without a mouthful of fodder. Even the stubborn Hastings agreed to lay over a day and rest their stock.

From the snow and ice of the Sierras they plunged down into the barren deserts of Nevada. As Jim stared back at the jagged peaks he felt a sense of awe. No one knew how lucky they had been to get through so early in the season. In that moment his distrust of Lansford Hastings was born.

Across a dry lake sink they followed the California Trail, a dim set of wagon ruts first traveled five years before. At night Digger Indians lurked about camp, but kept beyond rifle range. One evening they neared a hot spring, a boiling caldron of clear water. Panting with thirst, Lucky raced ahead and jumped in to drink.

"Lucky!" Jim cried.

He was too late. Lucky was scalded to death instantly. Heartsick, Jim buried him beside the trail. For thousands of miles, all the way from Wisconsin, they had traveled together. The loyal little dog had slept at the foot of Jim's buffalo robe almost every night for four years.

Flurries of snow fell daily as they rode northeast along the Humboldt River and passed between bleak mountain ranges. They saw no game to hunt. Horses and mules grew gaunt on the sparse grass. But Hastings refused to halt again and rest. At last they came to a fork in the river. Here the trail split. The wagon ruts turned left toward Fort Hall. A faint set of hoof tracks, made by Frémont's party, pointed straight ahead.

Hastings drew a map in the dirt. The straight route, he said, led due east to Salt Lake. It would save a long, unnecessary detour and weeks of travel.

The time had come for Jim to speak up. "You've never seen the salt desert east of here," he told Hastings. "Believe me, it's no shortcut for tenderfeet."

"Captain Frémont told me the route is safe," Hastings said. "There's plenty of grass and a good spring every twenty miles."

"The only other white man who ever took this route was Jed Smith, back in '27. He nearly died."

Hastings stiffened. "Do you doubt my word?"

"Frémont had Kit Carson for a guide and sixty tough mountain men in his party. You have women and children, Hastings. For their sake, stay on the main trail."

"I'm in command, Clyman. I'll go my way and you go yours."

Jim's jaw set. He felt no responsibility for Hast-

156

ings but he pitied the others. "No," he said. "I promised Sutter to help you folks. I won't quit now. On your own I don't think you'd reach Fort Bridger alive."

So they struck off on "Hastings' Cutoff." Never had Jim beheld such a desolate land—rocky plains and alkali flats where no spear of vegetation grew. There were no birds, no animal life, only lizards and scorpions. Sandstorms had covered much of the trail. While the column halted time and again he scouted ahead for tracks. Springs lay far apart and often the water was too bitter to drink. For two days they had no water at all.

Mirages shimmered on the horizon. Thick choking dust sent men and animals into fits of sneezing. But somehow Jim kept them moving. Tormented by heat and thirst, they plodded across a desert of pure white salt several inches deep. Now he recognized distant landmarks, peaks remembered from his voyage around Salt Lake. He heard the notes of a mockingbird, sweet music to his ears, the first in many days. On June 1, five weeks east of California, he reached the great blue lake itself.

Here on the southern shore they found a paradise of trees and sweet cold water. The animals rolled in the grass. The boys went swimming while their

157

elders stretched out in the shade. Once again Jim had led a party through without disaster, without loss of life. But his troubles with Lansford Hastings were not yet over.

14. A WARNING AND DISASTER

THE distance from Salt Lake to Fort Bridger was not much over a hundred miles, but in between lay the Wasatch Mountains. Although not as high as the Sierras or Rockies, this range was a jumble of peaks and canyons and deep rushing streams. In trying to find the shortest passage even Jim lost his way. Some gorges were so narrow they had to wade up the river bed, waist deep in water, or climb back and forth over boulders and steep-walled side canyons. Everywhere cliffs hemmed them in.

There was no trail. No wagons had ever crossed the Wasatch—only Indians and trappers on foot or horseback. But in six days they broke through the final rocky maze, topped the divide and hurried down into a beautiful wooded valley toward Fort Bridger.

159

But Jim Bridger and Louis Vasquez were gone, the post deserted. In dismay Jim stared at the empty corral. Many of his group were exhausted from the long hard journey. He had counted on buying supplies and fresh horses. Also he'd hoped to join some eastbound caravan for greater safety in crossing hostile Indian country between here and the next fort —Laramie. On top of this, some friendly Shoshones warned him that the Sioux were on the warpath.

To split the party and weaken it still more would be dangerous. But Hastings was determined. "I'm going on to Green River," he declared, "and establish a camp so I can be sure to intercept every emigrant wagon train."

Jim pointed out the risks. In case of Indian attack they would need every man for defense. They must all wait together until a stronger party came along. But Hastings refused to listen. "I'm a businessman," he said. "And my business is guiding settlers to California."

"You expect them to pay you?" Jim demanded.

"I do. Ten dollars a person."

"What!" Jim's temper boiled over. "You risked these people's lives in the Sierra snow. You risked them again in that salt desert. And now you'd leave them to the Indians. You're no guide, sir. You're a liar and a fraud!"

Hastings gave him an icy smile. "Name calling won't change my mind."

"Maybe not," Jim said grimly. "But I'll warn every emigrant I meet to keep away from your short-cuts."

Hastings departed with more than half the able-bodied men, leaving the others behind. Within a week, fortunately, a party returning from Oregon passed by, and Jim's small group joined them. They took two days to ferry across the swollen Green River on makeshift rafts, bypassing Hastings' camp, and pressed eastward along the Oregon Trail. Jim found Indian sign but no Indians. Two different nights their horses stampeded, but both times he rounded them up without a loss. They climbed over South Pass, the backbone of the nation, and started down the Mississippi watershed.

One evening he sighted a mass of running buffalo. This usually meant one of two things: emigrants or an Indian hunting party. Nobody slept much that night. But next day they rode over a rise and saw a long line of white-topped prairie schooners. It was the first westbound wagon train of 1846.

The emigrants sawed their teams to a stop and

gaped at these gaunt travelers. Questions poured forth. How far to water, to wood, to Oregon? Was the trail rough? What about Injuns? Could a man really find good cheap land? Jim told them all he knew. And to those few bound for California he gave the same firm advice:

"Keep on the Fort Hall trail. No matter what. Don't take any shortcuts across the desert. And don't try to cross the Sierras in the snow."

In return they told him the news. War at last had been declared between Mexico and the United States. He had missed the outbreak in California by a few days.

Every day he passed more wagon companies, strung out for miles across the dusty plains. This was the largest emigration yet—two thousand strong. At Fort Laramie he rode through the gate and someone called his name. It was James Reed, who had served with Jim and Abe Lincoln in the Black Hawk War. They chatted of friends back in Illinois, and of Abe, who'd been elected to Congress. Reed was full of questions too. Member of a California-bound train, he wanted to know all about the trail.

"Come have supper with us," he invited. "My friends will be anxious to hear what you have to say."

162

A Warning and Disaster

Around the cook fire Jim had a delicious treat, a cup of fresh milk, and tasted his first coffee since early winter. The emigrants plied him with food and hung on his every word. Children peeked out from behind their mothers' skirts and listened in awe. Here was a genuine, sure 'nuff Injun fighter. He'd been clear to Californy, and back!

Most of these people came from Springfield, Abe Lincoln's home town. Jim met their captain, George Donner, a wealthy farmer, his wife Tasmen and their five youngsters. Altogether there were thirty young children in the party. He inspected their oxen and wagons. The wagons were too heavily loaded, he said. They'd have to lighten up. Above all they must hurry, not waste a single day along the trail.

"You're already late in the season," he said. "How many miles a day do you travel?"

"Ten," Donner said. "Sometimes twelve."

"That's too slow, Mr. Donner. But maybe you can make it, if you keep on the Fort Hall trail."

"But, Jim, there's a nigher route," Reed protested. "It's no use to take such a roundabout course." He held up a book, a copy of *The Emigrant's Guide.* "This fellow Hastings says—"

"I know what he says," Jim cut in. "I just crossed that route with Hastings. It's barely possible to get

163

through before the snows if you follow the main trail. It may be impossible if you don't."

"I think we should take Mr. Clyman's advice," Tasmen Donner spoke up. "We've never met this Hastings man."

"Now, honey, you put the kids to bed," Donner told her. "I'll decide this."

Far into the night Jim pleaded with Donner and Reed. He told them of the Wasatch canyons, the salt desert, of the Sierras, where snow piled to a depth of forty feet. Jed Smith had gotten through. So had Kit Carson and Jim Clyman. But they were mountain men. George Donner wasn't.

Next morning two of the party came to Jim, one the ex-governor of Missouri. "You convinced us, Clyman," they said. "We're dropping out of Donner's train with our families. Going to Oregon instead."

Jim had argued and he'd begged. He could do no more. He rode on down the trail to Independence.

Later he learned that Lansford Hastings, angry because so many emigrants spurned his advice, sent a letter to George Donner by courier. In it he promised to guide the Donner party to California himself, over a short easy trail. But when they reached Fort Bridger, Hastings had gone with another train. As obstinate as ever, Donner turned off the Oregon Trail. Without a guide of any kind, he led his company of eighty-seven men, women and children across Hastings' "cutoff."

From that moment bad luck and disaster dogged them. Their wagons broke down. They quarreled and got lost in the desert. Indians ran off most of their oxen. A man died of thirst and a teamster was killed in a knife fight. Weakened by illness, heat and exhaustion, they crawled to the foot of the Sierras on November 1. The other emigrants, who had taken the "long way round," were six weeks ahead, safe across the mountains.

Suffering tremendous hardships, they got their few remaining wagons up to Truckee Lake, where Jim had camped that spring. One more day would see them over the summit. Three men started up the pass to break trail through the drifts. It began to snow again so they turned back to the lake. Next morning the snow was ten feet deep. They could not go forward. They could not go back. The Donner party was trapped for the winter.

Meanwhile Jim had rejoined his family in Illinois. "I'm like a bad penny," he told his brother. "Always turning up."

John smiled and shook his head. "I thought by this time you'd be married and settled down. But you'll never change, Jim. You ride off to cure a cold and come back four years later."

"This time I'm home to stay," Jim said.

Before long, however, he returned to Wisconsin to visit John Bowen. Everyone had read his reports in the Milwaukee press. The people of the state honored their pioneer hero by naming a town after him. But Jim had no desire for public acclaim. He passed the winter quietly at his friend's farm.

In those days there was no telegraph and no one had thought of the Pony Express. Most news from the Pacific Coast came by ship, a long slow voyage around South America, and then overland to Wisconsin. One late spring day Bowen returned from town with mail and the newspapers. "Didn't you meet a family named Donner last year?" he asked.

Jim nodded. "Fine people. I hope they got through to California all right."

Bowen handed him a newspaper. Forty members of the Donner party, almost half, had perished in the Sierra snows. Some had frozen to death, others had been killed and eaten by their starving companions. George Donner, his wife, his brother, many of the children— The survivors, after months of nightmare horror, had been rescued and carried over the mountains to Sutter's Fort.

166

A Warning and Disaster

The entire nation was shocked by the Donner tragedy, the worst in the history of the West. For years the memory of Lansford Hastings was to haunt Jim. Nor could he forget that night around the fire at Laramie, when Tasmen Donner had said to her husband, "I think we should take Mr. Clyman's advice."

"Don't blame yourself," Bowen told him. "You warned those folks."

Yes, Jim had warned them. He had warned hundreds of other emigrants too, along the trail that summer. No one can say how many people he saved from the same fate, for most of the emigrants *did* follow his advice.

The Mexican War drew to a close. As he had predicted, a few hundred determined Americans were able to capture California in a short campaign. It was now part of the United States. Oregon was soon to become a territory also. The dispute with Britain had been settled peacefully, by a compromise which gave America the present state of Washington. Within one year the United States had increased its size by a third.

The republic now stretched from ocean to ocean, from Puget Sound on the north to San Diego in the south. The Stars and Stripes floated over the Rockies, the Great Basin, the deserts of the Southwest. In his lifetime Jim had seen his country spread from the Atlantic seaboard to the Pacific coast.

In the spring of 1848 he received a letter from a California friend with word that part of the great Vallejo ranch, 80,000 acres near Napa Valley, was for sale for four thousand dollars. Jim had passed the place many times and knew it well. Before the American occupation it had been one of the largest ranches in the province, supporting thousands of cattle, horses and sheep. But what he remembered most were the stands of wild oats.

"You never saw the like," he told his brother. "A whole valley of natural oats, and not one single weed. That soil can grow anything."

"You're not fixing to go off again, Jim? At your age?"

"Five cents an acre. That's a bargain." A faraway look came into his eyes. He wasn't so old, only fifty-six. All that distant land came into his mind—the plains, the snowy peaks and redwood forests, the blue Pacific. He had to see it once again. "One more trip," he said. "This will be my last."

Within the week he was ready. He hurried off to Independence and the California Trail.

15. GOLD RUSH

F<small>OUR</small> years before, Independence had been jammed with emigrants preparing to go west. But this spring of 1848 only a few hundred gathered with their wagons. The fate of the Donner party had discouraged many from undertaking such a dangerous trip. In other years, too, a few mountain men had been available as guides. But now veterans like Black Harris, Bill Sublette, Tom Fitzpatrick and Kit Carson were busy for the Army, or elsewhere.

Word soon spread that Jim Clyman was in town. Lambert Mecombs, a Michigan farmer, sought him out. "Eighteen wagons in our party," Mecombs said. "Bound for Californy. There's my missus and me, and our nine young'uns. Most of them are married, with their own families. I'm the oldest, sixty-four. The youngest is a baby six months old."

Jim remembered that George Donner had been sixty-two. And there'd been no babies in the Donner train. "It's a hard journey for women and children," he warned Mecombs.

"I know, but we're hardy stock. Trouble is, we can't hire a guide. I won't risk my folks without a man along who knows the country."

"You won't find a guide in Independence."

"We're countin' on you, Mr. Clyman. I'll pay high wages."

The money meant little to Jim. But time was important. He must reach California before someone beat him to the Vallejo property. He had planned to join a small company of young men. Traveling fast on horseback, without wagons to hold him back, he could make the crossing in three months or less. An emigrant train required at least four. On the other hand, he sympathized with the Mecombs family. Rather than turn back they might be tempted to set out alone. How could he refuse people in such desperate need?

"I'll go on one condition," he said. "That you take the trail I show you and stick to it. I'm to have the final say on campsites, water, and how fast we travel. That's the only way you'll get there before first snowfall."

Mecombs thrust out his hand. "Agreed. Maybe my womenfolk won't like it, but from here on you're the boss."

As usual Jim found most of the wagons overloaded. He made the emigrants leave some of their heavy furniture and silverware and crockery behind. Several of the ladies complained bitterly but he held firm. No oxen could pull such loads through the Humboldt Sink and over the Sierras.

One morning he came upon a pretty, dark-haired young woman milking a cow. She was Hannah Mecombs, one of the unmarried daughters, and she'd protested hotly when Jim had made her get rid of a favorite mahogany chair. "Here, let me do that for you, miss," he offered.

Her black eyes blazed. "I never saw a man yet who could milk properly."

"I've milked quite a few in my time," he said.

"You go on about your business, Mr. Jim Clyman," she snapped. "This is woman's work."

Sheepishly he rode away. But after the train left Independence the emigrants began to appreciate him more. He knew the safest river fords, where to find firewood and how to protect their livestock from Indian raids. Quiet and patient, he kept far ahead on the trail as much as possible. One evening when he returned to camp Hannah Mecombs surprised him. "You've ripped your shirt," she told him. "I'll sew up the tear for you."

Jim, who once had sewed a man's ear back onto his head, grinned at her. "More woman's work?"

Hannah smiled back. "I'm sure you can mend clothes as well as any woman, but I don't have much else to do all day."

Several days later she gave him a new shirt, which she had cut out and stitched herself as the wagons jolted along. Jim floundered for words to thank her. Shy and flustered herself, Hannah said, "I—I owe you something for my rudeness the other day, Mr. Clyman. I hope it fits."

Beyond the Blue River one of the women gave birth to a baby girl. Jim held up the train so the mother and child could gain strength, but the baby died within three days. Lambert Mecombs buried the tiny body and marked the spot with a wooden cross. Long before South Pass they passed many other graves. Death had become commonplace along the trail.

Often Jim dropped back from his position at the head of the caravan to ride alongside Hannah's wagon. More and more of his spare time he spent in her company. At noon halts and around the evening fires he read poetry aloud to her—Milton, Byron, Shakespeare—or described the beauties of California. "You know, Jim," she told him, "Papa thinks the world of your advice. He's going to find land in the Napa Valley too. If you like it there, Papa says, it must be good."

Jim was pleased. By now he felt almost like a member of the family. And suddenly the truth dawned on him. He had fallen in love. Head over heels in love with gay, high-spirited Hannah, thirty years younger than himself. What would she do if he proposed to her? Laugh at him, of course. Out here on the plains she was friendly, but she'd never marry a man old enough to be her father. He tried to hide his feelings, unaware that his love was plain for all to see, especially Hannah.

Beyond Fort Hall he led them southwest into the Nevada deserts and along the Humboldt River, pushing through summer heat. This was the hardest stretch. The trail was littered with broken-down wagons, animal skeletons, with furniture and possessions cast off by other emigrants. Weary oxen could barely pull the food and water barrels over this barren land. The Mecombs looked their silent thanks at Jim, thinking of the Donners, who had passed this way in October two years before. No wonder he'd made them lighten their loads.

Late in August they camped at the meadows below the Sierras and peered up anxiously at the snow-tipped peaks. Could they get through? Jim said yes, and gave the order for a day of rest, knowing that each delay reduced his chances of reaching Napa in time to buy the ranch.

A small band of men rode down from the mountains and stopped to exchange news. They were Mormon soldiers, members of a battalion which had taken part in the conquest of California. Their enlistment ended, they were now returning east. "Big excitement over at Sutter's place," one said. From a leather pouch he poured out some bright yellow dust onto his palm. "Gold. Pure gold."

Jim and the emigrants crowded around. "Yep," the Mormon went on, "a fellow named Marshall made the strike."

"Not Jim Marshall, the carpenter?" Jim asked.

"That's the man. I was there the day he found it, working on his sawmill. Gold so thick you can dig it out with a spoon. Plenty for everybody."

"You're joshing us, mister," Lambert Mecombs declared.

"No, sir. Go see for yourself."

"Glory hallelujah!" Mecombs threw his hat to the ground and kicked it into the air. "I'll die a rich man yet!"

The train labored up the pass. At the lake, renamed Donner Lake, they camped among grim surroundings. Scraps of clothing and human bones, the last pathetic remnants of the Donner party, still lay scattered about the shore. Jim buried everything he could find. Emigrants had renamed the pass as well. Now the most famous pass in the West was Donner Pass—gateway to the California gold fields. Because a man named Donner didn't heed Jim Clyman.

On September 5 the Mecombs' caravan rolled down into the Sacramento Valley. Three days later they reached Napa, now a tiny settlement. And there Jim met another disappointment. He was several weeks too late. The Vallejo ranch had been sold already. "But there's other land here," Hannah consoled him. "It's all beautiful, just as you told us."

"No, I had my heart set on that piece," Jim said. "Maybe I'll try my luck mining gold."

The real reason he could not stay was that he couldn't bear to be near Hannah and see her marry some younger man. With two emigrants he turned back to Sutter's Fort. New Helvetia was a scene of wild confusion. Hundreds of gold seekers camped inside the walls. They slaughtered Sutter's herds for food, tore down his buildings for firewood, trampled his gardens and grain fields. The harassed Swiss was powerless to stop them.

"They have stripped me like a swarm of locusts," he wailed to Jim. "It is a disease, this gold fever. All California has gone mad."

"But there must be a fortune right on your doorstep," Jim said.

"Ach! These are lunatics, not men. I wish your friend Marshall had never found his accursed gold!"

Half the male population of Oregon had abandoned their farms and hurried south to dig for the precious metal. Soldiers deserted from the Army. Crews jumped overboard and left their ships to rot in San Francisco Bay. From Mexico and Hawaii, from far-off Chile and Australia, men set sail for California. And once the news reached the United States the greatest stampede in all history would get under way.

Gold! That magic word inflamed men's minds around the globe.

At huge expense Jim managed to buy a pick and shovel, a few supplies. With his friends he packed up the American River to a place the Indians called

176

Coloma. Red-shirted miners were digging frantically on every gravel bar and sand bank. At the sawmill he found James Marshall, who told him the story of his momentous discovery.

Seven months before, in January, Marshall finished his mill, he told Jim. But the big water wheel had been set too low. He had to deepen the tailrace so the wheel would turn. Marshall dug out a new channel, reopened the control gate and turned water in to wash out the loose mud and rock overnight. Making an inspection next morning, he found a nugget.

"My crew didn't believe it was gold," he said. "I didn't either at first."

But after Marshall found more he hurried down to the fort and told Sutter. Behind locked doors the two men tested samples with acid and weighed them on a scale. It was twenty-three-carat gold! "Sutter and I tried to keep it a secret," Marshall said. "But the word spread. Then it was like sitting on a volcano."

Jim congratulated him. It seemed only yesterday that this young carpenter, with nothing but a tool kit to his name, had ridden beside him through the Oregon wilderness. And now he had a chance to become one of the richest men on earth. But Marshall

177

said, "Not me, Jim. I found this site, I found the gold first. But I haven't been lucky since. Somebody always beats me to the best placer. I hope you do better."

Jim went several miles deeper into the Sierra, turned up a side canyon and located a claim. There were no courts, no laws. All a man had to do was drive his pick into the ground and declare, "This is mine." Jim had never mined before but he soon learned how to squat beside the stream with a shallow pan full of gravel. By turning the pan, shaking it gently, he let the water carry off the heavier particles. There on the bottom he stared at a few shiny flakes, his first gold.

The stories were true then! Every creek must be lined with gold. He hadn't quite believed it himself.

Some days he washed out as much as twenty dollars. Once he scraped out a rich pocket with his knife. His poke grew heavy with yellow dust. But the life was rough and hard and lonely. He spent hours in icy water, as he had as a young trapper. At night he slept in cold and dampness in the high canyon. Men around him grew sick from the diet of bacon and sourdough bread. More and more his thoughts turned to Hannah. Was she married yet?

Women, pretty young women, didn't stay single for long in frontier California.

Soon he realized he was spending more gold for food each day than he could mine. Prices of all supplies had soared to fantastic heights. Gold pans rose from twenty cents to sixteen dollars. A dollar for a single drop of medicine. Flour sold for four hundred dollars a barrel. A tent hotel in Coloma charged forty dollars for breakfast. When Jim heard this he threw down his shovel in disgust. "Sutter was right," he said. "This is crazy. I'm through with mining."

"What'll you do now?" his friends asked.

"I started out as a farmer and that's where I belong. On a farm. I'm going back to Wisconsin."

Hundreds of disappointed miners were quitting the mountains that fall. Most of the easy-to-find surface gold had been skimmed off by a lucky few. He returned to Sutter's Fort, planning to winter somewhere nearby, anywhere but Napa. Come spring he'd travel east by trail.

One of Sutter's clerks had tacked a number of letters to the trading post wall, which was the only "post office" in northern California. Jim was expecting no mail, but John Sutter called him into his private office. Eyes twinkling, he handed Jim a letter.

179

"I kept this aside for you, Jim," he said. "Because it looked special."

Jim's heart skipped a beat as he recognized the neat feminine writing. It was addressed to: *James Clyman, Esquire, Somewhere in the Gold Mines, per Mr. Sutter's Fort.*

Why had Hannah Mecombs written him? To announce her wedding? With trembling hand he tore open the envelope.

16. A HOME AT LAST

Her father, Hannah wrote, had bought some land. The family was busy getting settled. She hoped that Jim had found lots of gold. More important to Jim, she didn't mention any wedding plans. Maybe he still had a chance.

He rushed back to Napa, where the Mecombs welcomed him like a missing son. Lambert Mecombs' health had begun to fail, so Jim pitched in to help. He cleared land and set out crops. Every day he saw Hannah. But months passed before he could work up his nerve to propose.

Finally one spring evening he took her on a walk, to a hill overlooking the valley. New homes and farms had sprung up everywhere since his first visit. The wilderness, where once he had hunted grizzlies, had given way to the plow. But he felt no regret, no itch to move on. Here, at last, he knew he wanted to put down roots. After all his wanderings across the West, this was home.

"Hannah," he blurted, "will you marry me?"

"Oh, Jim!" Her eyes shone and then brimmed with tears. "Of course I will! But I was afraid you'd never ask me."

"You mean—"

"I fell in love with you way back in Kansas, Jim. Mama said it was a scandal the way I set my cap for you." She laughed. "I nearly died when you went off hunting gold."

He didn't tell Hannah how close he had come to leaving without seeing her again. They made plans for a summer wedding. He was determined that his bride should have the best of everything to start housekeeping. "We don't even have a set of dishes," she teased him. "You made me leave all my china and furniture in Independence."

Jim went to San Francisco. In this booming port supplies were scarce and almost as expensive as in the gold fields. No matter. Nothing was too good for his Hannah. He bought every piece of crockery in town and freighted them back to Napa. For years he liked to chuckle and remind her, "We're eating off gold plates. Each one cost a fair-sized nugget."

A Home at Last

On August 22, 1849, they were married, this slender young emigrant woman and the grizzled mountain man. It was the first wedding in Napa. Relatives and friends came to the ceremony from hundreds of miles.

That same year the Gold Rush reached its peak. Eighty thousand newcomers poured into California, by sea and over Donner Pass. Some made fortunes in the mines. Others, like John Sutter and James Marshall, lost everything and went bankrupt. Lansford Hastings dropped from sight into obscurity. John Frémont, now a colonel, was elected the first senator from the new state.

The following spring another of Jim's dreams came true. Part of the old Vallejo ranch, which had lured him back to California, went up for sale. He bought it. Now he had land, his own beloved land to farm. He built a house and planted an orchard. Hannah gave birth to their first child, a daughter they named Lydia. Jim's life had never been so rich and full.

Happy busy years went by. Four more children, two boys and two girls, were born. Jim bought another tract of land to enlarge his farm and added a dairy herd. He pruned and planted, plowed and harvested, while Hannah ran the house and milked the cows. "A long time ago," she said, "I told you no man could milk a cow. And I haven't changed my mind."

California had been admitted to the Union as a free state but back east the slavery issue grew into a national crisis. In 1856 Frémont ran for President on an antislavery platform, and was defeated. But four years later the voters sent Abe Lincoln to the White House on the same platform. Jim heard the news with amazement. He'd never imagined that some day his friend would become President of the United States. Throughout the Civil War that followed he was torn between North and South. But though Virginia born, he remained loyal to the Union.

Then cruel tragedy struck his growing family. His youngest daughter, seven-year-old Martha Ellen, came down with scarlet fever. No serum had been developed for this dread disease yet. He and Hannah nursed the little girl around the clock, but she died. Before they had recovered from their grief another fever epidemic swept the countryside, taking the two boys, James and Philip. Not long before Christmas the next year they lost fifteen-year-old Mary Irene. Four of their five children—all but Lydia—were gone.

During his long life Jim had suffered many a

bitter blow. But now he had to call on all his courage to bring Hannah through this crisis. The big empty house seemed as deathlike as a tomb. He prayed to God for strength, and then went to his wife with a plan.

"Hannah," he said gently, "quite a few children have been left orphans, without any folks to look after them. You and me, we're the other way 'round now."

"You want to adopt a child, Jim?"

He took her in his arms. "There's a purpose in everything the Good Lord does. Maybe this is His test of the love in our hearts. I'd like to help some of those little ones."

For the first time in weeks Hannah's eyes brightened. "So would I, Jim. It's wrong not to want to go on living. We have so much to be thankful for."

Sharing their grief, drawing strength from each other, they adopted three girls as foster daughters— Alice, Geneva and Edna—and took them into their home. Once again the house buzzed with life, with the laughter and gaiety of children. Slowly the scars healed. Then their own Lydia met and married a young man in the neighborhood. Before long she presented Jim with his first grandchild.

He passed his eightieth birthday and, hearty as

ever, worked each day in his fields and orchards. His farm became one of the most productive in the area. Many honors came to him. A steady stream of guests enjoyed his hospitality. But gradually he left more of the strenuous chores to others. He liked to sit in the warm sun on his porch, writing verse and studying American history.

"Jim," Hannah told him one day, "a newspaper editor wants to publish those diaries of yours. The ones you kept crossing the plains. He says they're important historical documents."

Jim laughed. Important? Those notebooks he'd scribbled in so many years ago? He'd forgotten they existed.

"Don't laugh at me, Jim Clyman," she said tartly. "No man living has seen more history than you. All the things you've done, the famous men you've known."

"I didn't do much," he protested. "I just happened to be there."

But to please Hannah he dug his diaries out of an old trunk. Then the editor persuaded him to write down his memories of his fur-trapping days. There were no eyewitness accounts of the early fur trade, the editor said. That was so, Jim supposed. Not many of his old friends had been able to read, or even to write their names. The few who could had been too busy catching beaver and fighting Indians. And now only one other that he knew—Jim Bridger— was still alive.

The work went slowly. He wanted to search his mind and record each event exactly as it happened. Also, his eyesight was failing. He had to write in large letters on a slate on his lap. And the grandchildren were always around begging him for more stories. "Tell us about George Washington, Grandpa," or "Tell us how you wrestled Abe Lincoln."

Come to think of it, he *had* seen and done a lot. So many things had happened, so many changes. Where it had taken him months to cross the country on horseback, trains now whizzed through in days. News flashed across the continent over the telegraph in hours. The Indians had been subdued and put on reservations. A man could travel the plains with never a fear of losing his hair.

One day while he was chopping wood a chip flew up and hit his eye. He could no longer see to write. Feeble and in pain now, he dictated the rest of his memoirs to Lydia. On Memorial Day he was invited to give a speech at Napa in honor of the nation's war dead. This always had been an important occasion to Jim, but he was too weak to attend. Instead he wrote a poem:

> Strew flowers o'er the hero's head
> Who for your country fought and bled.
> He fought for equal rights for all,
> Let raining flowers o'er him fall.
> He died your country's life to save,
> Strew flowers o'er the hero's grave.

He knew his own end could not be far off, but he faced it calmly, as he had faced all of life. Each evening Hannah read the newspaper aloud to him. This one night her voice faltered. "Read it to me," he insisted.

"It's Jim Bridger," she said. "He died last week on his farm in Missouri."

Jim closed his eyes. He thought of the battle with the Rees, more than half a century ago. He remembered the first rendezvous, tall yarns around the campfire, the buffalo surrounds, swapping oxen at Bridger's Fort. And now Old Gabe, Jim Bridger himself, was gone. The next to the last of the mountain men.

He sank rapidly now. Two days after Christmas, 1881, a month before his ninety-first birthday, he passed over the final divide. He'd reached the end of the trail—the last to rejoin Jed Smith, Ashley, Fitzpatrick, Sublette, Kit Carson, Black Harris, Hugh Glass and all the others of that immortal band.

Afterward Hannah could say proudly to her grief-stricken family, "Don't mourn for Jim. He died a contented man. He wanted you to be happy. He always thought of others first."

Jim Clyman had been so modest about his accomplishments that for many years he remained an obscure, almost forgotten figure. Then historians began to study his reports. He never thought of himself as an explorer. No stream or mountain peak or western landmark was named for him. As he said, he just happened to be there.

But he was the first man to travel part of the Oregon Trail. He was with the group that discovered South Pass, and made use of it as a trade artery. He led the first white men over the pass that became the modern transcontinental highway and railroad route across Wyoming. He was the first to explore Salt Lake. For any one of these achievements he deserves recognition.

Intensely patriotic, he fought in two wars and emerged as a highly respected officer. He took part in so many Indian campaigns and battles, against a dozen different tribes, that the Indians themselves came to respect him. And yet he was no "Injun hater" like many frontiersmen. The policy of extermination was against his moral principles, and he always treated them fairly.

Pathfinder, soldier, surveyor, he served America in many ways. He helped to open Illinois and Wisconsin for settlement. During the emigrations of the 1840's he saved untold settlers from disaster, as he tried to save the Donner party. His honest factual letters and newspaper reports on Oregon and California inspired hundreds of his countrymen to pull up stakes and move west.

His life spanned almost a century, a century in which he saw the United States expand from the original thirteen of George Washington's day to a great continental power, from an infant revolutionary republic to a mighty nation stretching from Atlantic to Pacific. A roll call of Jim's friends and contemporaries reads like a page of American history: Leavenworth, Lincoln, Dodge, McLoughlin, Marshall, Sutter, Frémont. These men *were* history. Their lives and deeds intertwined with his.

From a penniless Virginia farm boy he rose to success in several business careers—fur trapper, land scout and rancher. But making money was not all-important to him. For forty years he roamed the West, seeking new country and breaking trail through the wilderness. Not the least of his contributions is the picture of that era, which he left in his diaries and journals for us today.

He lived in a violent period of history, among constant dangers, yet he was a man of gentleness. He wrote poetry, loved nature, felt deeply about the wonders he saw and described. He loved his country, too, and foresaw the time when its vast empty spaces would be filled with farms and towns. And although he preferred solitude to civilization, he put the good of people first. His life is one long record of helping those who needed help, often at great personal sacrifice.

Perhaps one trait looms above all. As a youth he learned many a harsh lesson of pioneer survival. From the moment he entered the West as a trapper, he became a leader. No one doubted his ability. This quiet simple man was born to lead other men. From the tough fur brigades, along the rugged Oregon Trail to the brawling gold fields of California, he left his mark. A symbol of all that was best on our frontier, Jim Clyman stands as a shining example to generations of Americans.

James Clyman: American Frontiersman are by permission of the California Historical Society